HSC
Health & Safety
Commission

Health and Safety Commission
ANNUAL REPORT
1992/93

STATISTICAL
SUPPLEMENT

HSE BOOKS

CONTENTS

    *   These tables are also included in the Annual Report.

INTRODUCTION

1 This new Statistical Supplement replaces an annual supplement to the Employment Gazette[1,2,3] in which health and safety statistics have been published for the last few years. It also includes the provisional figures for 1992/93, the first occasion on which these have been published. They are also set out in summary in the Annual Report.The next section gives the background to the statistics. This is followed by commentary on occupational injuries, dangerous occurrences, gas safety, enforcement statistics and occupational ill-health. The supporting tables have been grouped together, and include more time series of data than the supplement to the Employment Gazette. More detailed statistics are available on certain industries and types of accident, and on request from the Statistical Services Unit (Annex I).

2 The injury and dangerous occurrence figures given in this report are based on injuries reported under the Reporting of Injuries, Diseases and Dangerous Occurrences Regulations 1985 (RIDDOR). These Regulations came into effect on 1 April 1986 and replaced the Notification of Accidents and Dangerous Occurrences Regulations 1980 (NADOR). Changes in definitions, particularly the definition of a major injury, mean that many of the statistics derived from reports made under RIDDOR are not comparable with those previously reported under NADOR. Most of the time series therefore start in 1986/87. The definitions of injuries reportable under RIDDOR are given in Annex II.

3 The RIDDOR and enforcement statistics for 1992/93 are provisional (denoted by 'p' in the tables). Final figures are normally about 2.5% higher because of late reports and because fatalities include deaths up to a year after the date of an accident. To help interpretation, broad estimates of the final injury rates are given below. The commentary concentrates on the finalised figures, ie those up to 1991/92, but where appropriate includes references to the likely trends in the 1992/93 figures, as indicated by the estimated final rates and analysis of the figures already reported.

Table A Injury incidence rates (per 100 000 employees): provisional figures compared with the best estimated final results, by main industrial sector

Sector	1992/93p			1992/93ef		
	Fatal	*Major*	*Over-3-day*	*Fatal*	*Major*	*Over-3-day*
Agriculture, forestry and fishing	7.1	162.4	548.2	7.8	165	558
Energy and water supply industries	4.9	193.9	1617.6	4.9	194	1640
Manufacturing	1.4	123.4	1104.7	1.4	125	1120
Construction	7.3	239.5	1356.0	7.5	241	1368
Services	0.6	50.9	460.7	0.7	53	479
All industry	1.2	78.8	659.5	1.3	81	677

4   The figures for fatal injuries are based on RIDDOR statistics and other sources of information to ensure that the statistics on fatalities are virtually complete. However it is possible that a small number of fatalities, mainly to members of the public, may be missed due either to the particular circumstances of the accident or a lengthy gap between the accident and the ensuing fatality. This should not affect the consistency of the data series over time.

5   In contrast to the comprehensive information available on fatalities, a supplement to the 1990 Labour Force Survey (LFS) confirmed HSE's previous concerns that non-fatal injuries are significantly under reported: less than a third of reportable non-fatal injuries at work are being reported. Full details are given elsewhere[4], but the levels of reporting vary both between employment sectors and employees and the self-employed. Estimates of the levels of reporting are:

For employees in:

Energy	:	80%
Construction	:	around 40%
Manufacturing	:	40%
Services	:	23%
Agriculture	:	19%
For the self-employed	:	5%

Thus while the provisional non-fatal injury rate for 1992/93 for injuries to employees reported under RIDDOR was 740 per 100 000 employees, the estimated total level of reportable injuries was 2300 per 100 000 employees with rates varying across the main industry sectors from 2000 in services to 3100 in manufacturing, 3500 in construction and 3800 in agriculture.

6   Two key features emerged from the LFS research. First, reported accidents are a good indicator of the relative order of risks by industry. Second, the physical types of injury in reported accidents are representative of those indicated by the survey. This means that reported injuries, though incomplete, still reflect the overall picture of all accidents in terms of relative risks and physical injuries.

7   A further set of questions on work-related injuries is to be asked in the 1993/94 LFS and thereafter on a regular basis. These questions will provide a global figure for injuries including those not reportable under RIDDOR. They will also provide the opportunity to examine any changes in the level of reporting, although it is thought unlikely that reporting patterns have influenced the trends in non-fatal rates.

8   The commentary and tables of occupational ill-health statistics in 'Occupational ill-health' are based on a wide range of sources. This section collects together the available data to quantify the extent of all types of occupational disease as accurately as possible.

NOTES ON SECTIONS

Injuries by severity and industrial sector
Kind of accidents

9   The injury statistics presented in these sections were reported under RIDDOR to all enforcement authorities.

Nature and site of injuries
Age and sex of injured people

10   These sections relate to injuries reported to HSE's Field Operations Division Inspectorates and local authorities. Injuries in the off-shore oil and gas industry, in mines and on railways are not included because of incompatabilities in the data. Tables 7-10 cover 1987/88 to 1992/93p only as nature and site of injury was not coded for local authorities in 1986/87. Tables 13 and 14 are the exception, as information on the sex of the injured person is available for all enforcing authorities (except the Railways Inspectorate) from 1988/89.

Dangerous occurrences

11 Incidents which are reportable as dangerous occurrences are defined and listed in RIDDOR. This list is selective, the aim being to obtain information about those incidents which have a high potential to cause death or serious injury whether or not someone is actually harmed.

Gas safety statistics

12 This section gives details of the numbers of incidents and injuries relating to the supply and use of gas (including both piped gas and bottled LPG) as collected under RIDDOR.

Enforcement action statistics

13 Action taken by HSE Inspectorates and other enforcing authorities, including local authorities, to ensure compliance with the Health and Safety at Work Act 1974, and associated legislation, ranges from general advice through to the issue of enforcement notices and prosecution. This section gives figures for notices and prosecutions.

Occupational ill-health

14 The principal sources of data and areas of concern in occupational health are introduced in this section, followed by commentary arranged on a disease by disease basis.

INJURIES BY SEVERITY AND INDUSTRIAL SECTOR

1 In 1991/92, 184 500 injuries were reported to the HSC/E enforcement authorities, including local authorities. Of these:

170 400 were to employees, of which 297 were fatal;
3000 were to the self-employed, of which 71 were fatal;
11 100 were to members of the public, of which 105 were fatal.

2 The total number of injuries was the lowest reported under RIDDOR. Reported injuries to employees and members of the public were 5% and 24% lower than in 1986/87 respectively, while the number of reported injuries to the self-employed in 1990/91 was nearly twice the 1986/87 level.

Figure 1 Injuries by employment status 1986/87 - 1991/92

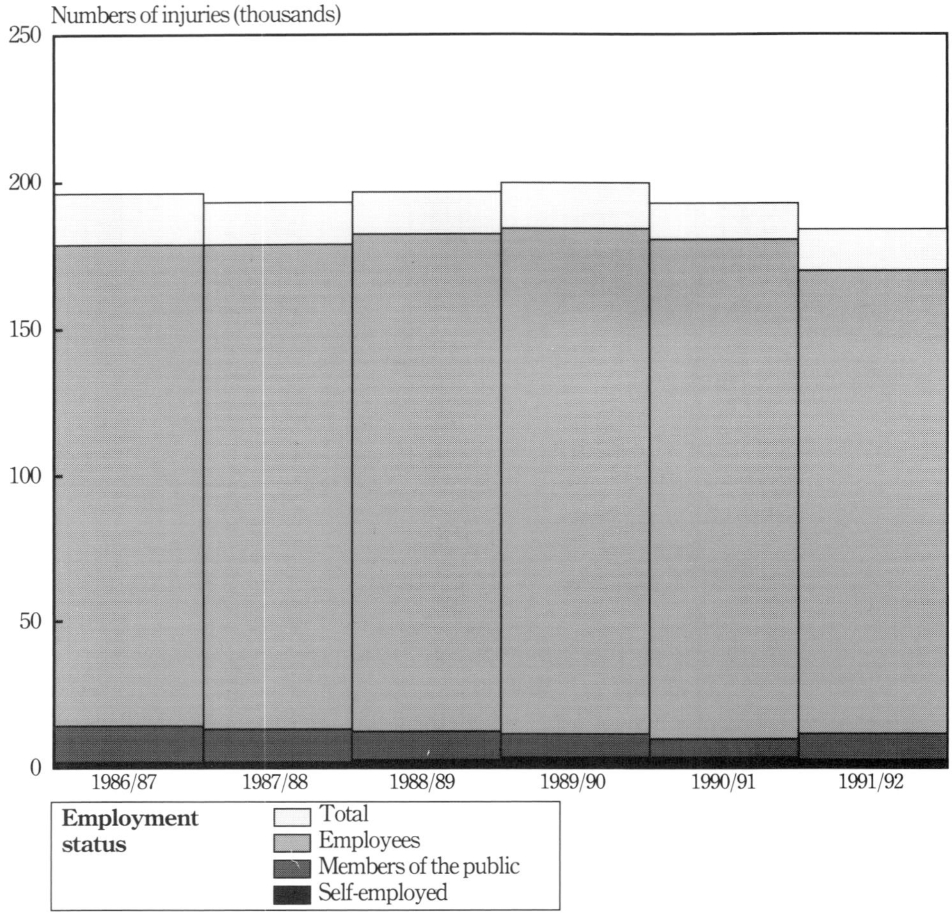

Injuries to employees

FATAL INJURIES

3 In 1991/92:

there were 297 fatal injuries to employees, a decrease of 14% from the previous year;
the fatal injury rate was 1.4 fatalities per 100 000 employees, a reduction of 12% from the previous year.

4   These figures represent the lowest number of fatalities and the lowest injury rate since RIDDOR was introduced in 1986/87. It is the second successive year the fatal injury rate has fallen, after remaining constant during the second half of the 1980s (excluding the fatalities in the 1988 Piper Alpha disaster). Provisional figures indicate that a further reduction is likely in the number of fatal injuries in 1992/93 and the final fatal injury rate for 1992/93 is expected to be 1.3 per 100 000 employees.

Figure 2   Fatal injuries to employees 1981-1991/92

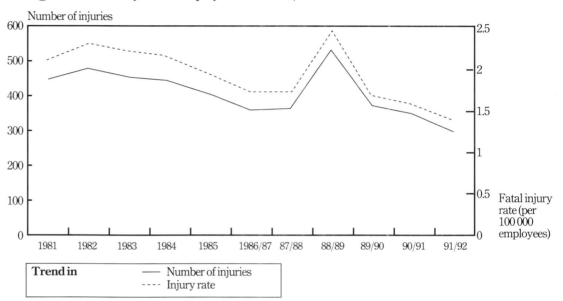

Over a longer time span and despite some extension of the requirement to report fatalities, the 1991/92 rate is one quarter of that reported in 1961 and less than half of that in 1971.

5   Part of the decrease in the fatal injury rate is accounted for by changes in the pattern of employment since the mid-1980s. Since 1986/87 there has been a 10% increase in the number of employees in the service industries (which have a low rate of injury) and a fall in the numbers working in the more hazardous sectors: energy (down by 19%) and manufacturing (down by 11%). In particular, the number of employees in the coal extraction industry, where the fatal injury rate in 1991/92 was 17 per 100 000 employees, has halved.

6   Over the six year period 1986/87 to 1991/92, the fatal injury rate:

in construction has decreased each successive year, except in 1987/88, with a continuation of this downward trend in 1992/93;

in manufacturing has been less stable, but has dropped in each of the last two years, with the 1992/93 rate expected to be lower again, although only marginally below that for 1991/92;

has remained virtually constant in the service sector;

in both energy and the agricultural sectors is more likely to fluctuate because of the small proportions of employees working in these areas and hence a greater affect on the rate of a relatively small increase in injuries. In energy the fatal injury rate in 1991/92 was the highest in the six year period (excluding the fatalities in the Piper Alpha disaster) but substantially lower in 1992/93, whereas the fatality rate in agriculture in 1991/92 was the lowest in the past six years, with the 1992/93 rate expected to be around the average for the period.

7   See Table 2 for further details.

Figure 3   Fatal injury rates to employees by industrial sector 1986/87-1991/92

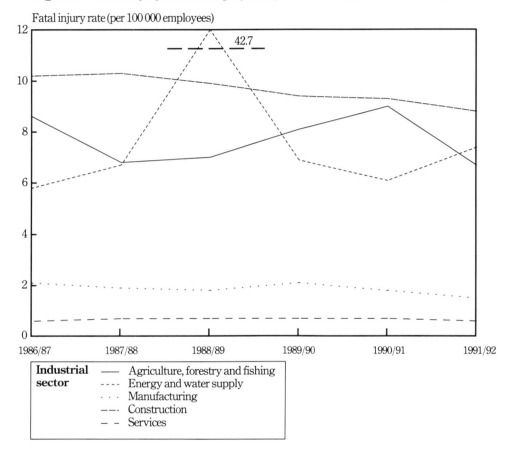

8   Looking at particular industries the fatal rate averaged over the six year period 1986/87 to 1991/92 was highest in:

	Average rate per 100 000 employees
extraction of mineral oil and natural gas	86 *
extraction of minerals/ores other than coal, oil and gas	24
forestry	20
coal extraction	14
railways	11

*   Includes the 167 fatalities in the Piper Alpha disaster. The average rate without these deaths would have been 18.

MAJOR INJURIES

9 The number of reported major injuries to employees dropped to 17 600 in 1991/92, a decrease of 12% compared with the 20 000 reported each year between 1987/88 and 1990/91.

Both the number and the rate of non-fatal major injuries was lower in every industry sector in 1991/92 than in 1990/91. See Table 3 for further details.

The rate for fatal and major injuries combined fell from 91 to 83 per 100 000 employees.

Table B   Fatal and major injury rate per 100 000 employees: 1986/87 - 1992/93p

	1986/87	*1987/88*	*1988/89*	*1989/90*	*1990/91*	*1991/92*	*1992/93p*
Agriculture	145	169	158	150	169	157	169
Energy	336	289	308	260	246	231	199
Manufacturing	147	144	146	147	138	130	125
Construction	293	287	296	308	291	281	247
Services	58	56	53	54	56	50	51
All industries	101	96	94	93	91	83	80

OVER-3-DAY INJURIES

10 The number of reported over-3-day injuries also fell in 1991/92 to 153 000 compared to 161 000 in 1990/91 and the incidence rate for over-3-day injuries fell in each of the past two years, having remained virtually constant in the late 1980s. The recent improvement in the over-3-day injury rate can be attributed totally to the changing patterns in employment.

11 Over the six-year period, over-3-day injury rates have:

fallen substantially each year in the energy sector;
shown a tendency to rise in agriculture and manufacturing but to fall in construction.

12 See Table 4 for further details.

Injuries to the self-employed

13 There were fewer fatal injuries in 1991/92 to the self-employed than in each of the previous four years and the fatal injury rate was the lowest in the last five years.

The fatal injury rate for the self-employed remained substantially higher in agriculture than in any other sector, with 13 deaths per 100 000 workers compared with two for industry as a whole.

Figure 4 Proportion of fatalities among the self-employed by industry sector 1991/92

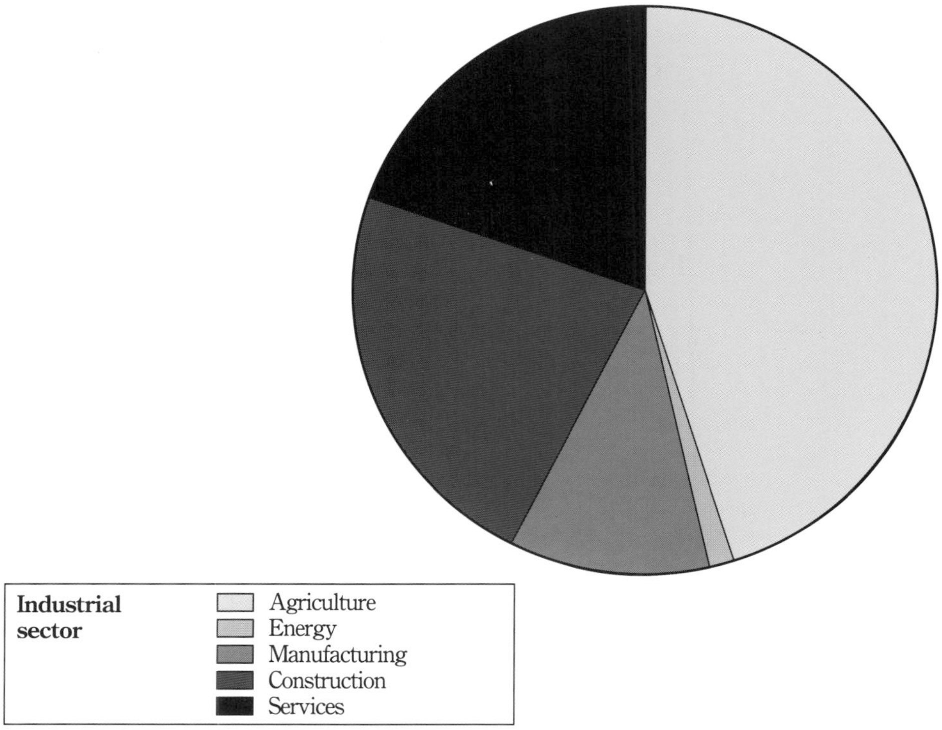

Industrial sector		
	☐	Agriculture
	☐	Energy
	▨	Manufacturing
	■	Construction
	▦	Services

14 The provisional figures for 1992/93 indicate a substantial drop in the fatal injury rate for self-employed agricultural workers. However, this must be seen against a background of relatively small numbers of accidents and workers (the latter being estimated from the Labour Force Survey), so small changes in either can lead to marked fluctuations in the rate. The fatal injury rate for the self-employed is likely to remain highest in workers in the agricultural sector.

15 The fatal injury rate to self-employed workers in the construction industry fell for the second successive year, although there is a possibility that some of the fatalities to the self-employed are being coded as employees, thus artificially reducing the rate.

16 The number of reported non-fatal major injuries and over-3-day injuries also fell to 1100 and 1800 respectively. This represents a reversal of the trend seen over the last two years when the numbers had risen. Nearly 70% of both major and over-3-day injuries to the self-employed were to workers in the construction industry.

Injuries to members of the public

17 There were 105 fatal injuries to members of the public in 1991/92, the lowest figure since 1986/87, although this reduction was not maintained in 1992/93.

Most fatal injuries to members of the public were in the service sector.

18 The reported number of non-fatal major injuries (11 000) to members of the public was lower than the numbers reported in the late 1980s, although slightly higher than in 1990/91. Virtually all of these injuries occurred in the service sector and over half in education.

Injuries to employees

19 Over half of the fatal injuries to employees in 1991/92 where the kind of accident was recorded were caused by:

> falls from a height (29%);
> being struck by a moving vehicle (18%);
> being struck by a moving, including falling, object (12%).

Figure 5   Fatal injuries to employees by kind of accident 1986/87 - 1991/92

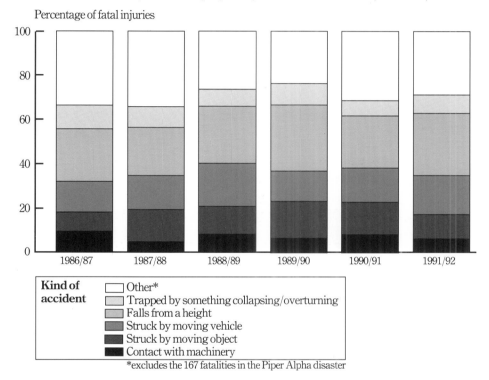

Percentage of fatal injuries

Kind of accident	
☐	Other*
▨	Trapped by something collapsing/overturning
▨	Falls from a height
▨	Struck by moving vehicle
▨	Struck by moving object
■	Contact with machinery

*excludes the 167 fatalities in the Piper Alpha disaster

This pattern has changed little since 1986/87, except for 1988/89 when the Piper Alpha disaster occurred.

Table C   Fatal and major injuries to employees by kind of accident 1991/92

Kind of accident *	Fatal	Major
Falls from a height	83	3997
Struck by moving vehicle	52	578
Struck by moving including a flying or falling object	33	2157
Trapped by something collapsing/overturning	25	191
Contact with moving machinery	19	1472
Slip,trip or fall on same level	2	5628
Injured while handling, lifting or carrying	2	1098
Other causes	81	2476
Total	297	17 597

* For kinds of accident causing 5% or more of fatal or major injuries

20 Compared with the average for the period 1986/87 to 1990/91, for those fatalities where the kind of accident was recorded:

falls from a height accounted for a greater proportion in 1991/92 (29%) but the provisional figures indicate that this fell to 23% in 1992/93;

being struck by a vehicle accounted for a slightly higher proportion in 1991/92, but the 1992/93 figure is likely to be more in line with the earlier period;

being struck by a moving, including falling, object accounted for a lower percentage in both 1991/92 and provisionally in 1992/93;

5% were caused by contact with electricity, the lowest proportion since 1986/87 but this reduction was not maintained in 1992/93 when the figure is likely to be about twice as high, and above the average for the late 1980s.

21 Slips, trips or falls on the same level and falls from a height are by far the commonest causes of major injury. In 1991/92, they accounted for 32% and 23% of major injuries respectively and similar proportions in 1992/93.

22 The proportion of major injuries accounted for by slips, trips or falls is now higher than in the late 1980s having risen to 32% in 1990/91 and 1991/92 compared with an average of 28% in the previous four years and is likely to remain at the higher level in 1992/93.

23 The proportion of non-fatal major injuries caused by contact with machinery fell slightly in 1991/92 and looks likely to have fallen again in 1992/93, so that the figures for both years are likely to be below the average for the previous five years.

24 More than a third of reported over-3-day injuries in 1991/92 were injuries sustained while handling, lifting or carrying and the proportion appears to be increasing slightly. The proportion of injuries caused by being struck by a moving object dropped slightly in each of the three years prior to 1991/92 and looks likely to be lower again in 1992/93. Nearly a third of the remainder were slips, trips or falls.

25 See Table 5 for further details.

Injuries to the self-employed

26 The majority of fatal accidents to self-employed people were also falls from a height, being struck by a moving vehicle or by a moving object. Together these kinds of injury accounted for 45 of the 71 fatalities to the self-employed in 1991/92. A further nine deaths were caused by contact with electricity or electrical discharge; an unusually high number compared with four in 1990/91 and provisionally four in 1992/93.

27 Nearly half of the major injuries and a quarter of over-3-day injuries to the self-employed were caused by falls from a height, mainly because of the proportionately higher number of self-employed workers in the construction industry.

28 The proportion of injuries caused by slips, trips or falls accounted for 15% of over-3-day injuries for the self-employed, compared with 20% for employees.

29 See Table 6 for further details.

Figure 6   Fatal and major injuries to employees and the self-employed by kind of accident 1991/92

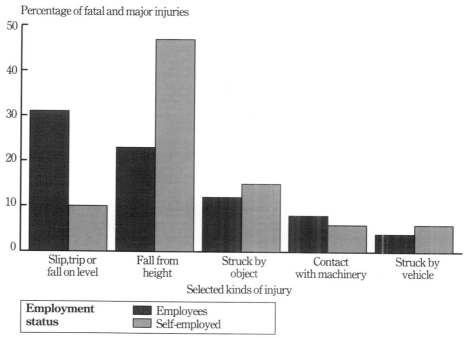

Percentage of fatal and major injuries

Selected kinds of injury

Employment status — Employees / Self-employed

Figure 7   Over-3-day injuries to employees and the self-employed by kind of accident 1991/92

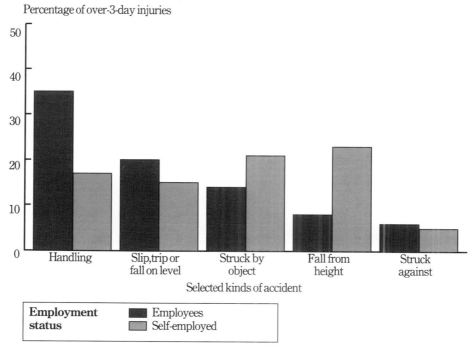

Percentage of over-3-day injuries

Selected kinds of accident

Employment status — Employees / Self-employed

NATURE AND SITE OF INJURIES

Nature

30 Where the cause of injury was specified, contusions and fractures continued to be the most common causes of fatal injuries for both employees and the self-employed. Not surprisingly, multiple injuries were also a significant cause of death.

In 1991/92, there were 50% fewer fatal injuries to employees caused by contact with electricity than in either of the previous two years, and the lowest number since RIDDOR was introduced. However this reduction was not sustained in 1992/93.

31 Fractures accounted for three-quarters of non-fatal major injuries to both employees and the self-employed in 1991/92. There has been a slight but steady rise in the proportion of accidents involving fractures since 1987/88 and a decrease in the proportion of amputations.

In 1991/92, 6.7% of accidents to employees were amputations, compared with 9 % or more in each year in the late 1980s.

Figure 8 Fatal and major injuries to employees and the self-employed by nature of injury 1987/88 - 1991/92

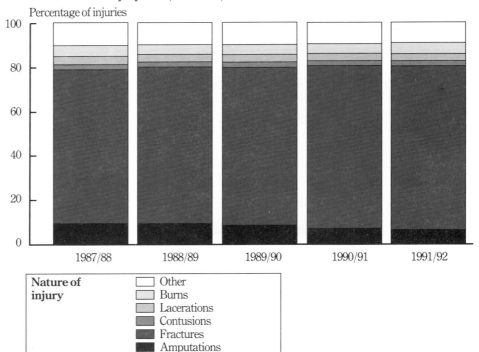

32 For over-3-day injuries to employees, sprains and strains accounted for 40% of injuries and contusions for a further 18%. For the self-employed, fractures continued to account for the highest number of injuries, with sprains and strains, contusions, and lacerations and open wounds contributing over 15% each.

33 See Tables 7 and 8 for further details.

Site

34 For fatal injuries in 1991/92 the head was the most common specific site of injury, accounting for nearly a quarter of all fatal injuries. However:

Over 40% of fatal injuries to both employees and the self-employed affected several or general locations.

The decrease in the number of head injuries which occurred in 1990/91 to 62 from over 80 in each of the years 1987/88 - 1989/90 was maintained and may be further reduced in 1992/93.

In construction the fatal injury rate due to head injuries fell each year from 3.1 per 100 000 employees in 1988/89 to 1.9 in 1991/92 and this trend is likely to have continued in 1992/93.

Table D Head* injuries in construction

		Number of injuries		All injury rate per 100 000
	Fatal	Major	Over-3-day	employees
1986/87	32	122	466	64
1987/88	42	109	480	63
1988/89	32	127	498	65
1989/90	26	140	527	65
1990/91	21	103	377	49
1991/92	18	100	366	51
1992/93p	15	72	310	46

*   Excluding injuries to the eyes, ears and other parts of the face only.

35 For major injuries and over-3-day injuries the most common site remained the upper limb, accounting for over half of all reported major injuries. For major injuries over a third were to the wrist, whereas for over-3-day injuries the most common site was fingers and/or thumbs.

Contrary to the trend in the previous three years, major injuries to the ankle decreased in 1991/92. A further reduction looks likely for 1992/93.

In the construction industry, the decrease in major head injuries seen in 1990/91 was maintained in 1991/92 and the number looks likely to fall again in 1992/93

36 There were fewer major injuries to most sites of the body in 1991/92 than in 1990/91, the exceptions being injuries to the hand, eye and ear.

37 Figure 9 shows the distribution of all reported injuries by site for 1991/92; detailed figures for site of injuries are given in Tables 9 and 10.

Figure 9 Proportion of all reported injuries to employees by site of injury 1991/92

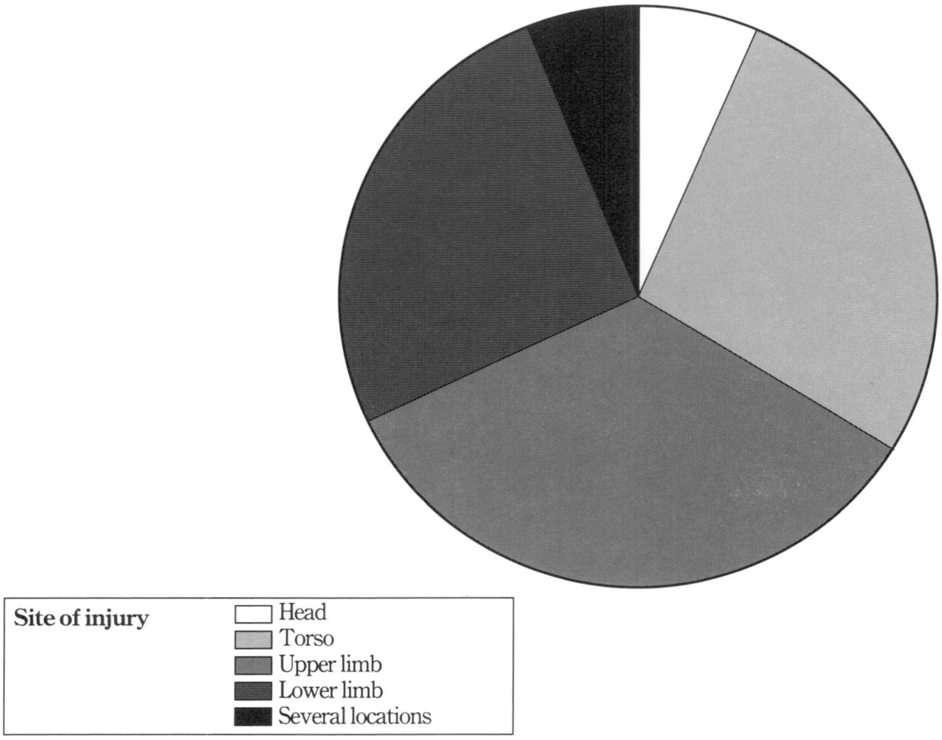

Site of injury		
	☐	Head
	▨	Torso
	▨	Upper limb
	▨	Lower limb
	■	Several locations

Table E Sex of fatally injured people 1986/87 - 1991/92

		1986/87	*1987/88*	*1988/89*	*1989/90*	*1990/91*	*1991/92*
		Numbers of people injured					
Fatal	Men	291	297	304	330	293	246
	Women	6	3	5	7	5	9
Non-fatal major	Men	14 716	14 627	14 500	14 815	14 240	12 541
	Women	4211	4106	4088	4421	4684	4196
Over-3-day	Men	117 153	116 586	118 747	122 813	119 254	110 941
	Women	25 243	27 481	29 492	33 139	33 458	34 507

38 Virtually all employees who are fatally injured at work are men. Three-quarters of both non-fatal major and over-3-day injuries are also to men. This reflects the pattern of employment where men are more likely to work in higher risk occupations.

39 However, the proportion of injuries occurring to women is rising slowly due largely to an increase in the proportion of over-3-day injuries to women.

40 There is a noticeable difference between the patterns of injuries by age for men and women. For men, the highest numbers of injuries occur in their twenties. For women, more injuries occur to those in their fifties. Figure 10 shows the distribution for fatal and major injuries; the picture for over-3-day injuries is similar.

41 See Tables 11 and 12 for further details.

Figure 10 Fatal and major injuries to male and female employees, by age of injured person 1991/92

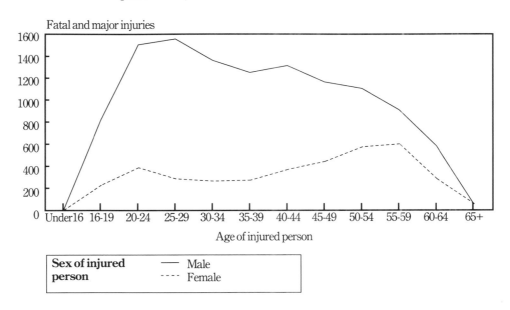

Table F Injury rates for men and women per 100 000 employees

		1988/89	*1989/90*	*1990/91*	*1991/92*
Fatal	Men	4.3	3.0	2.7	2.6
	Women	**	0.1	**	0.2
Non-fatal major	Men	132	133	126	120
	Women	41	42	44	54
Over-3-day	Men	1083	1099	1060	1018
	Women	293	317	319	330

** Less than 0.05

42 The injury *rates* for men and women show the same pattern with the non-fatal major injury rate for men being over twice that for women and the over-3-day injury rate being three times as high.

43 The rates also show an overall trend of rates rising slightly for women whilst those for men have fallen over the past three years.

44 For men, the non-fatal major rate has fallen steadily over the past few years in energy and over the past three years for which finalised figures are available in manufacturing and construction. There has also been a steady reduction in the rate of over-3-day injuries in the energy sector. These trends look likely to continue in 1992/93.

45 See Table 13 for details.

46 For women, there were steady rises in the rates for both non-fatal major injuries and over-3-day injuries in the service sector for each year from 1988/89 to 1991/92. These parallel the rises in injuries in the service sector to both men and women from 1988/89 to 1990/91, but do not reflect the reduction seen in the total figure in 1991/92. In contrast, the non-fatal major rate for women in services in 1992/93 looks likely to be well below that for the average of the previous four years when the overall figure looks likely to be in line with the average for 1989/90 to 1991/92.

47 See Table 14 for details.

DANGEROUS OCCURRENCES

48 Part 1 of the Schedule to RIDDOR relating to the reporting of dangerous occurrences contains a general list for all places of work and Parts II, III and IV contain lists of dangerous occurrences which are specific to mines, quarries and public transport railways respectively. Trends in the numbers of dangerous occurrences have to be treated with some caution as there are no estimates of the extent to which dangerous occurrences are unreported.

The total number of dangerous occurrences in 1991/92 was 3676, 7% lower than in 1990/91, 12% lower than in 1986/87 and over 10% lower than in each of the other years since 1986/87. It is likely that the number will drop further in 1992/93.

49 The number of dangerous occurrences notifiable in relation to any place of work was 9% lower in 1991/92 than in 1990/91. Failure, collapse or overturning of lifting machinery etc and uncontrolled or accidental release of a potentially harmful substance or pathogen continued to be the most significant categories, accounting for nearly half of all dangerous occurrences in 1991/92. There was a reduction of 10% or more in the number of dangerous occurrences reported in the following categories:

explosion or fire and stoppage for over 24 hours;
unintentional ignition or explosion of explosives;
explosion, collapse or bursting of any closed vessel;
failure of breathing apparatus in service;
failure or collapse of lifted freight container;
accidental collision between a train and other vehicle.

50 The only category of dangerous occurrence to increase substantially in 1991/92 compared with the previous year was plant or equipment coming into contact unintentionally with overhead electric cables.

The number of incidents notifiable in relation to mines and quarries both decreased substantially.

51 Figure 11 shows the number of dangerous occurrences notifiable in relation to any place of work, mines and quarries and other classifications; further statistics on dangerous occurrences are given in Table 15.

Figure 11 Dangerous occurrences 1986/87 - 1991/92

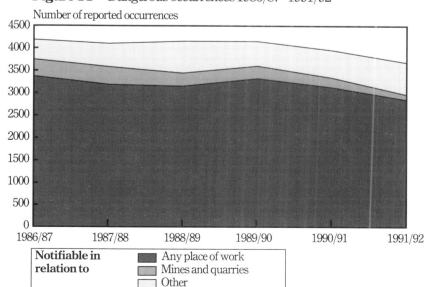

140 incidents relating to the supply and use of flammable gas were reported in 1991/92, the second highest number since RIDDOR was introduced in 1986/87. However the 1992/93 figure is likely to be lower.

41 related fatalities occurred in 1991/92, the lowest in any year since 1986/87.

52 The number of gas incidents reported has fluctuated over the past six years, with an average of 133 incidents being reported. There has been a small reduction in the number of fires and explosions caused by gas appliances in recent years, with these incidents forming a smaller proportion of the total. This may be due, in part, to the general fitting of flame safeguard devices to appliances such as cookers. It may also be a reflection of a general improvement in installation practices.

53 The numbers of carbon monoxide poisonings need to be treated with some caution as this type of poisoning is not always easy to diagnose. However, the provisional figures for 1992/93 indicate a rise in the number of incidents for the third successive year, and an increase in the number of fatalities. The figures underline the need for regular maintenance of gas appliances and HSE will continue to work with the gas industry to raise public awareness about gas safety.

Figure 12   Injuries caused by supply and use of flammable gas 1986/87 -1991/92

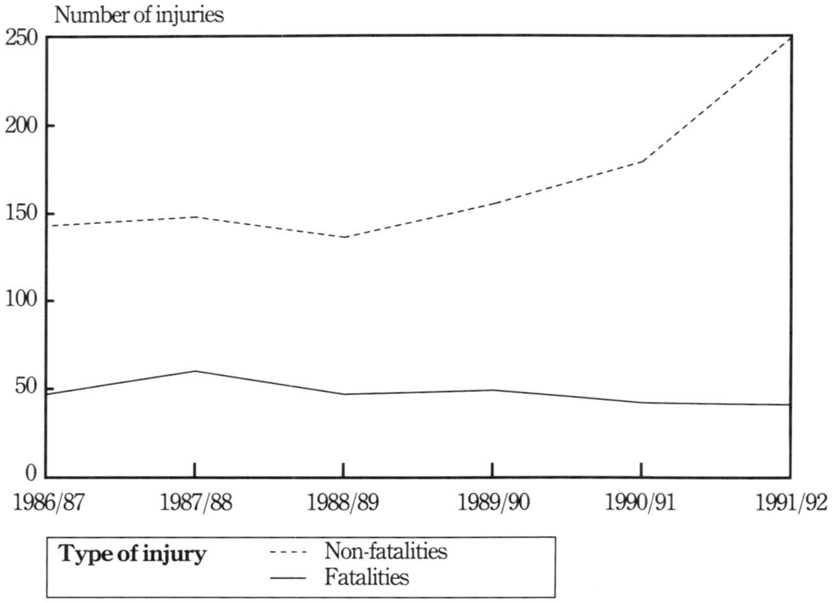

54 Detailed statistics are given in Table 16.

55 The total number of returns for dangerous gas fitting notifications fell by 16% from 1990/91 to 1764 in 1991/92.

56 Over a third of dangerous gas fitting notifications involved a boiler, and a further 15% involved a gas fire (other than decorative/fuel effect). This pattern has remained similar since 1988/89.

57 The sharp rise in the proportion of notifications involving decorative gas log and other effect appliances seen in 1990/91 was maintained in 1991/92.

58 See Table 17 for further details.

59 The commonest section of the installation at fault over the past four years has involved the ventilation of an open flued appliance, accounting for over a third of notifications in 1991/92.

60 Faults in open-flued appliances (including flues and ventilation) and in installation pipes have accounted for over 60% of notifications in each year since 1986/87.

61 See Table 18 for further details.

62 The main reason for the fault continued to be the manner of installation, accounting for over 60% of notifications. Modifications or alterations remained the second highest contributory factor.

63 See Table 19 for further details.

64 Gas leaks and the inadequate removal of products of combustion each accounted for nearly a quarter of the notifications in 1991/92. However the 1992/93 figure looks likely to be substantially lower. The number of incidents involving inadequate ventilation in 1991/92 was the lowest for the last four years.

65 See Table 20 for details.

Enforcement notices

Over 34 000 enforcement notices were issued in 1991/92, the latest year for which figures for all enforcing authorities are available. This compares with 25 800 in 1990/91 and 15 500 in 1981.

66 The number of notices issued has increased steadily since 1985. The increase from 1990/91 to 1991/92 was accounted for by the number of notices issued by local authorities, probably linked to the enforcement regime associated with, but not necessarily under, the Food Safety Act and comments made in an Audit Commission report on LA Environmental Health Departments.

67 The most common type (four out of five notices) was an improvement notice which requires employers to put right a contravention of health and safety legislation within a specified time limit. The increase in the number of improvement notices accounted for nearly all of the increase in the total number of notices issued.

Figure 13 Enforcement notices issued by type of notice 1981-1991/92

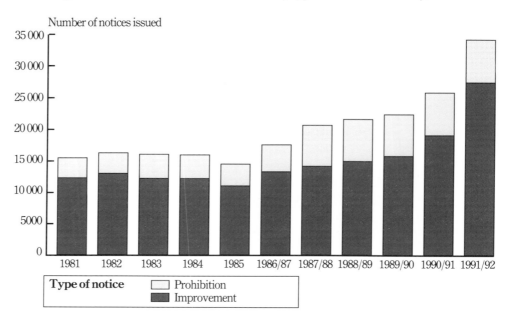

68 Over 90% of prohibition notices in 1991/92 were immediate prohibitions. These stop a work activity until an imminent risk of serious personal injury is eliminated. The number of immediate prohibition notices increased sharply to about 6000 in 1987/88 and 1988/89 when there were major enforcement initiatives aimed at small construction sites. Since then, the numbers have remained at this level.

69 See Table 21 for further details.

70 The number of enforcement notices issued by HSE's Field Operations Division increased each year from 1986/87 to 1990/91 but was 3% lower in 1991/92. The decrease was largely due to a drop in the number of notices issued in the agricultural sector, but has to be seen in the context of a move towards addressing a root cause of poor health and safety in organisational deficiencies rather than specific defects.

The number of enforcement notices issued in 1991/92 increased in the service sector by more than a quarter from 1990/91 and in the construction industry by 20%.

71 See Table 22 for further details.

Prosecutions

72 Prosecution statistics are based on the informations laid by inspectors before magistrates in England and Wales, and charges preferred in Scottish courts.

73 The number of informations laid by HSE Inspectorates and HSC Agencies in 1991/92 was 2400, slightly above the average number of around 2300 in the previous 10 years. The provisional figure for 1992/93 is about 300 lower.

74 The conviction rate in 1991/92 was 88%, slightly higher than either of the previous two years and representing a return to the level of 1987/88.

75 Although trends in the average levels of fines for offences convicted against health and safety legislation are complicated by a small number of very high fines awarded against some companies by the higher courts, whether the single large fines are included in the figures or not, the average fine per conviction has risen in each of the last four years:

The number of prosecutions by local authorities in 1991/92 (783) was the highest since 1981.

76 88% of prosecutions by local authorities resulted in convictions, above the rate for most of the previous ten years.

77 See Table 23 for further details. Note that where a single information attracted a fine of £100 000 or more the average excluding this exception is shown in a footnote.

78 For prosecutions by HSE's Field Operations Division only:

44% in 1991/92 were in manufacturing, a similar proportion to previous years;
the number of prosecutions in agriculture has decreased steadily since 1986/87;
the numbers in the service sector increased substantially in 1989/90;
the numbers remained around the same level for 1990/91 and 1991/92 but dropped again in 1992/93.

79 Generally, the average fine following a conviction increased between 1986/87 and 1991/92 in all industrial sectors.

80 In 1991/92, the average fine rose substantially in energy, construction and the service industries, even discounting two large fines against Shell UK Ltd and British Gas plc.

Fines in agriculture were less than half of those in other industrial sectors throughout the late 1980s and even less in 1991/92.

81 See Table 24 for further details.

OCCUPATIONAL ILL-HEALTH

82 The term occupational ill-health covers a wide range of conditions, from those which are unequivocally work-related, such as lead poisoning and asbestosis, to those conditions with multiple causes, only some of which are occupational in origin and for which the link to workplace exposures may not be so clear. Conditions in this second category range from those with a well established occupational link, such as lung cancer in asbestos workers, to the more speculative, such as 'Sick Building Syndrome'.

Sources of information

83 No single data source gives complete coverage of the cases of occupational disease occurring in the workforce. Cases of the well-established 'prescribed diseases' are recorded under the Industrial Injuries Scheme administered by the Department of Social Security, which continues to be our main source of statistical information. Additional sources of data for conditions not covered by this scheme, or known to be seriously under-counted in the number of awards qualifying for disablement benefit, are constantly being sought. RIDDOR data provides an additional potential source for most of the prescribed diseases, but is known to suffer from substantial under-reporting. Death certificates and mortality studies are a source of data for the usually fatal conditions. Schemes set up to monitor cases, for example of work-related respiratory disease (SWORD) and skin disease (EPIDERM), as they appear in specialists' or GPs' consulting rooms are now providing valuable data in their areas. A record of some work-related infections is maintained by the Communicable Disease Surveillance Centre (CDSC). Periodic surveys such as the 10-yearly morbidity statistics from general practice and decennial supplements on occupational mortality can contribute further information. Studies of specific risks supplement this general information.

Labour Force Survey

84 Data obtained from the supplementary 'trailer' questionnaire to the 1990 Labour Force Survey (LFS) has also provided a comprehensive source for assessing the prevalence of a wide range of occupational morbidity in the workforce as a whole. As it is based on respondent's own perception of the link between their occupation and ill-health, information on areas of ill-health not covered by existing data sources has been obtained, and when repeated it will allow insight into change in the patterns of occupational ill-health in these areas.

85 The 'trailer' questionnaire asked all adult respondents to this survey in England and Wales whether they had:

'In the last 12 months, suffered from any illness, disability or other physical problem that was caused or made worse by (their) work'.

Follow-up questions established the nature of the illness and the job that was thought to have given rise to it; whether the work was thought to have caused the condition or simply made it worse; and the number of days sick leave in the year due to the complaint.

Industrial Injuries (II) Scheme - background

86 The only comprehensive and consistent data for occupational disease in the UK are provided by the records of awards for 'prescribed disease' under the Industrial Injuries

Scheme administered by the Department of Social Security (DSS). Although the figures are affected from time to time by changes in the rules defining benefit entitlement, the system has the advantage that all cases are individually examined and validated. The figures represent an absolute lower limit to the numbers of cases occurring. Trends can, with some caution, be taken to reflect real changes in incidence although they can also be affected by changes in propensity to claim benefit.

87 There are, however, two important discontinuities in the Industrial Injuries Scheme data, which should be borne in mind when reading the disease commentaries which follow. The first is between 1982/83 and 1983/84, when injury benefit was - for the generality of claimants - replaced by Statutory Sick Pay. The second follows the introduction, for claims lodged after 1 October 1986, of a new general rule under which only those with disability assessed at 14% or more qualify for benefit (pneumoconiosis, mesothelioma and byssinosis are excepted from this rule). Cases with lesser disability are still recorded, and until October 1990 could qualify for Reduced Earnings Allowance if their earning potential was impaired. This change has substantially reduced the numbers qualifying for disablement benefit, and seems also (with the notable exceptions of Vibration White Finger (VWF) and asthma) to have reduced the numbers making claims.

88 A further factor to be borne in mind when interpreting data drawn from the compensation system is the value of the compensation available.

89 Between 1971 and 1983 there was a substantial fall in the relative value of Injury Benefit (payable for sickness absence due to *prescribed* disease), as compared to Sickness Benefit (payable for any sickness absence). In money terms the difference between these two benefits was held constant at £2.75 per week throughout this period. The impact of this on individuals' propensity to claim injury benefit is difficult to ascertain, but is likely to have affected the numbers making claims during this period. The value of disablement benefit - for which there is no corresponding 'alternative' benefit - has not changed so drastically, and has in fact increased in real terms from the equivalent (revalued to April 1993 prices) of £66/week in 1971 to £91.60/week (for 100% disablement) in 1993.

90 Two major components of the total of diseases assessed under the Industrial Injuries Scheme are occupational deafness and VWF. Cases of occupational deafness are collected by the DSS separately from the rest of the prescribed diseases (other than those assessed by Special Medical Boards), and diagnosed cases of VWF have lately been at exceptionally high levels, a probable consequence of increased awareness of the possibility of compensation. If these are excluded, the numbers of II cases of diseases not dealt with by Special Medical Boards fell from 1680 in 1985/86 (the last year before the restriction of benefit payment to cases with 14%+ disablement) to 761 in 1988/89, but rose in each of the following years, to 1563 in 1991/92. Part - perhaps all - of this increase is likely to be due to improvements in the system of statistical returns from DSS local offices introduced in April 1990 (midway through the 1989/90 II year, which runs to September).

The overall picture

91 Nearly 6% of adults reported suffering from a work-related illness in the 12 months to the spring of 1990, as recorded in the Labour Force Survey, and half of these were seen as caused by work. This implies a total of 2.2 million cases of work-related illness in England and Wales in a 12 month period. 1.3 million of these cases, with a margin of error

of 50 000 either way - 95% confidence limits - were considered to be 'caused' by work. Not all of these cases were serious: nearly half of the cases reported by people who had worked during the previous 12 months had taken no time off because of their illness. The 700 000 who did take sick leave on account of their illness took an estimated total of 13 million days off work. An estimated 750 000 retired and unemployed people reported being affected by the longer term consequences of work-related illness.

92   The potential damage to the nation's health from work-related illness is demonstrated by the continuing legacy of harm from past exposure to silica, coal dust and asbestos. These substances are now strictly controlled, and there is reason to hope that the risks from current exposure levels are acceptably low. However the number of new cases of lung disease (pneumoconioses, pleural thickening and cancers) due to these substances, but particularly asbestos, which are awarded disablement benefit each year continues to rise and is now over 1500 a year.

93   For asbestos, a rough estimate of the numbers of premature deaths due to asbestos-related cancer can be based on the national numbers of deaths due to mesothelioma: this suggests a total of up to 2750 deaths annually (based on 1991 figures), and rising. (About 600 of these cases receive II benefit). Figures for compensated cases of asbestosis also continue to show a strong underlying upward trend and have more than doubled since 1981.

94   For the pneumoconioses other than asbestosis, numbers have remained fairly steady now since 1984, fluctuating around an annual average of about 400 cases. This is well below the average for previous decades, but there has been no indication of a resumption of the downward trend apparent in the figures up to 1984.

95   The effects of past levels of noise in the workplace continue to be reflected in the diagnosis of around 1000 new compensatable cases of occupational deafness a year; a total of about 13 000 people were receiving disablement benefit in April 1992. This compares to a prevalence estimate of over 100 000 people suffering deafness or other ear problems thought to have been caused by their work from the Labour Force Survey. The past use of vibrating hand-held tools has also led to the diagnosis annually of well over 2000 cases of Vibration White Finger since 1989/90.

96   Turning to diseases where the effects of exposure are more immediately apparent, about 1000 cases of occupational asthma were seen by specialist chest or occupational physicians in 1992, and an increasing number of new cases of this disease are being diagnosed each year under the II scheme, with a broadening of the list of prescribed agents with the addition of an 'open category' in 1992 adding to this effect.

97   Musculoskeletal conditions affect a very large number of people, and work activities will often contribute to the problem. This is an area where it is very difficult to assess the extent of the occupational contribution, both at the individual level and overall. The affected individual is in many ways the best placed to make this judgement, and in the responses to the LFS trailer self-reports of musculoskeletal conditions far exceeded those of any other disease category. The estimated number of prevalent cases 'caused' by work from this survey was 593 000, of which 50 000 were of Repetitive Strain Injury and most of the remainder (300 000) were related to back problems. An annual estimate of 20 000 new cases of work-related Carpal Tunnel Syndrome diagnosed by GPs reinforces the impression

that musculoskeletal disorders are widespread. The limited range of conditions covered by the II scheme - still resulting in over 1000 cases of assessed disablement in 1991/92 - provide an absolute minimum estimate of the number of more serious cases.

98 Numbers of cases of occupational dermatitis are also probably substantially greater than have ever received benefit from the II scheme. Data from three separate surveys (including the LFS) all produce estimates of the annual number of cases of between 50 000 and 100 000.

99 The long-term consequences of trauma and poisoning, and of stress/depression were both represented in the LFS by an estimated prevalence of just over 100 000 cases each, 'caused' by work. Higher rates of morbidity following traumatic injury and poisoning at work in older and in inactive groups imply a strongly persistent nature for many of these cases, along with a substantial movement out of employment. On the other hand most cases of stress/depression were recorded in the recently working population, implying a reversible and generally non-persistent effect.

100 Occupations recorded by respondents in the Labour Force Survey as causing (or exacerbating) the illness were coded using a modified version of the occupation orders of the standard Office of Population Censuses and Surveys (OPCS) occupational classification. The modifications brought together occupational units with similar work conditions. Figure 14 gives data for the occupational groups, showing for each group:

(a) the estimated national (England and Wales) prevalence of cases, with the number 'caused' by work and the number 'made worse' by work shown separately; and

(b) the risk of work-related illness for each occupation group relative to an 'all occupations' baseline of one.

Figure 14   Relative risk and estimated numbers of prevalent cases of self-reported work-related illness by occupation category

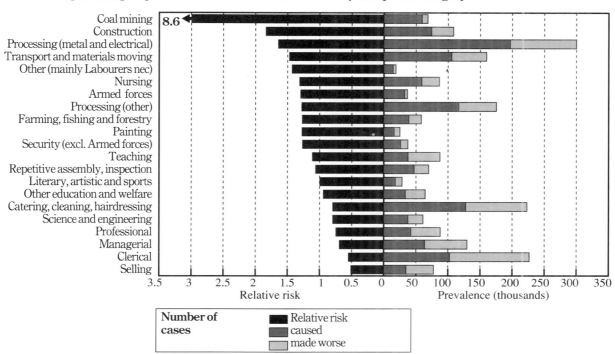

101 The occupations reporting the highest overall rates of work-related illness were coal mining, construction, metal and electrical processing, occupations involving transport and materials moving and unskilled labourers.

102 Further details about the figures and how the rates were derived can be found in the recently published HSE Research Paper No 33, *Self-reported work-related illness*[5]. The reported 9-fold risk for mining relative to the general population should be treated with particular caution because of the difficulties in defining a denominator for this rapidly contracting industry.

103 In what follows we shall take diseases - or related groups of diseases - in turn, summarizing the appropriate data from the Industrial Injuries Scheme in a series of Figures, together with data from other sources when this is available. The general commentary is followed by tables for each of the main data sources, displaying the detailed underlying figures. Additional information on the sources and the detailed figures are given in the final section, 'Notes on tables'.

Detailed commentary

PNEUMOCONIOSIS (OTHER THAN ASBESTOSIS)

104 The rules governing the award of Disablement Benefit for pneumoconiosis have not been affected either by the abolition of Injury Benefit or by the restriction of benefit to cases with higher levels of disability. Knowledge of the disease and of the arrangements for compensation are widespread within the main affected industries: mining, quarrying,

Figure 15   Pneumoconiosis (other than asbestosis)

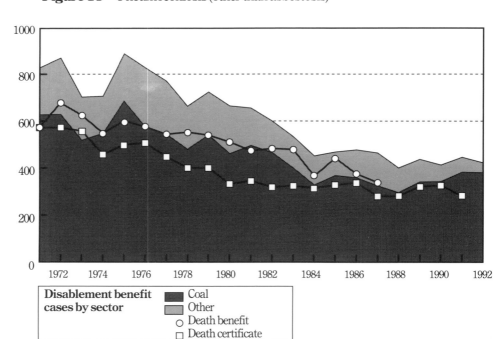

Note: from 1990 disablement figures do not include cases awarded by Medical Appeals Tribunals (see Table 28)

foundries and potteries. The figures for compensated cases can therefore be expected to give a reasonably accurate reflection of the incidence of disease. This is borne out by the similar trends shown by the three available series: Disablement Benefit, Death Benefit and deaths with pneumoconiosis as their registered underlying cause (Figure 15).

105 Pneumoconiosis is a disease that takes a long time to develop. Only in exceptional cases will the disease be produced in less than ten years, and most cases appear between 15 and 30 years from first exposure. This means that the cases now coming forward largely reflect the working conditions of ten and more years ago.

106 As might be expected, coal mining still accounts for the majority of compensated cases (93%) outside the asbestos industry, most of these occurring amongst the retired. The proportions of workers diagnosed before retirement age is higher in the other industries affected, although absolute numbers are much lower.

107 Due to the long and variable delay from first exposure to the onset of detectable disability, the broad trend of the figures is more informative than any detailed fluctuations from year to year in drawing conclusions about changes in the incidence of these diseases; and, by implication, changes in the conditions that produced them. In these broad terms, the figures show a long-term decline in pneumoconiosis other than asbestosis, at least until 1988 since when there has been a slight upturn in the numbers of cases counted, principally amongst ex-coal miners.

ASBESTOS-RELATED DISEASE

108 Four diseases have been unequivocally linked to asbestos exposure: asbestosis, mesothelioma, lung cancer and pleural thickening. By definition, every case of asbestosis is due to asbestos; the association with mesothelioma is also very strong, though there is a 'natural' background incidence of about 2 cases/million/year (ie about a hundred cases per year nationally). For lung cancer the situation is different, since the predominant cause of this cancer is smoking, and asbestos exposure increases the risk of disease both in smokers and non-smokers (though, in absolute terms, much more so for smokers than non-smokers). Lung cancer is a prescribed disease in connection with asbestos provided the

Figure 16   Asbestosis

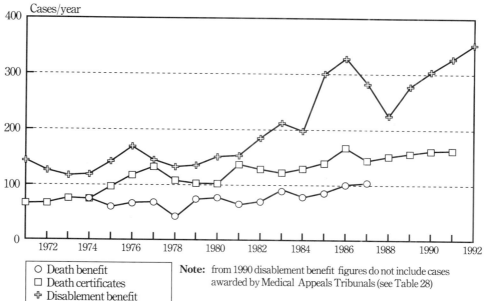

Note: from 1990 disablement benefit figures do not include cases awarded by Medical Appeals Tribunals (see Table 28)

○ Death benefit
□ Death certificates
✚ Disablement benefit

individual shows some other clinical sign of asbestos exposure (asbestosis, or pleural thickening), as well as evidence of occupational asbestos exposure. All three of these diseases display long delays from first exposure to diagnosis: typically 15 to 25 years for asbestosis and up to 40 years for lung cancer and mesothelioma.

109 For *asbestosis* (Figure 16), Disablement Benefit awards show a continuing, but erratic upward trend. They fluctuated between 100 and 200 per year while rising slowly through the 1970s and early 1980s, but then rose to a peak of 329 in 1986, falling back to 225 in 1988, and rising again to a maximum of 354 in 1992. Throughout this period awards of death benefit also grew from around 70 in the early 1970s to just over 100 in 1987, the last full year for which claims could be made.

110 Death certificates mentioning asbestosis (excluding those also mentioning mesothelioma), show a somewhat stronger increase from similar levels in the mid-1970s to around 163 in 1991.

111 From 1974 to 1986 the proportion of disablement benefit awards for asbestosis falling into the different percentage disablement categories remained very stable. In 1987 the percentage of awards assessed at 10% or less (Table 29) fell from about a third to about a fifth of all awards. In a similar way the median age of first diagnosis had been constant at just under 60 up to the beginning of the 1980s, it then began to rise slowly and is now above 65. These two fairly recent trends might indicate a tendency for individuals to claim benefit later in the course of the disease than previously.

112 However, it is still the case that relatively higher numbers of younger (pre-retirement age) workers are affected by asbestosis than is the case for pneumoconiosis in the coal mining industry.

113 Claims for disablement benefit currently being made (for 1991 and 1992) indicate that while about 85% still relate to dates of first exposure up to the end of the 1950s, with first exposures peaking between 40 and 50 years ago, 11.7% relate to more recent exposure in the 1960s. There is evidence in the numbers coming through to suggest at least a levelling off of reported first exposures in this decade, following a steep decline in numbers relating to first exposures during the 1950s. This could reflect either increased use of asbestos during this period or an effect of peak latency for this disease at between 20 and 30 years. A small number (3%) - which reflects however a relatively short latency period for the people involved - relate to first exposures after the implementation of the 1969 Asbestos Regulations. Only diagnosed cases for which a year of first exposure was recorded at medical examination have been used in deriving the above estimates.

114 The figures for *mesothelioma* (Figure 17 and Table 32) show a steady upward trend between 1971 and 1984. This was interrupted in 1985 when the number of deaths fell from 626 to 615. In 1986 and 1987 there were steep increases of 14% and 15% respectively.

115 The rate of increase slowed down between 1987 and 1989 and finally fell by 2% in 1990 from 899 to 881. This fall was followed by a steep increase in 1991 when the number of deaths rose by 15% to 1017.

116 The typically long delay between first exposure to asbestos and death from mesothelioma means that the deaths now occurring are in the main due to exposures in the 1940s and

Figure 17 Mesothelioma

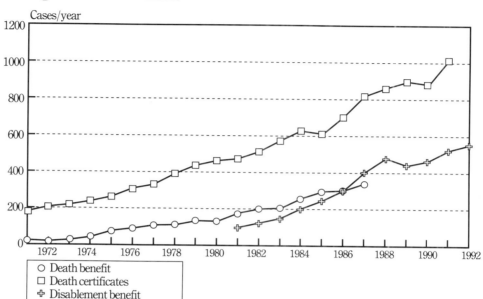

○ Death benefit
□ Death certificates
✛ Disablement benefit

Note: 1987 is last full year for Death benefit
Disablement benefit figures not available for years to 1980

1950s, although there are recent indications that the incidence of mesothelioma in successive generations of men up to those born around 1950 is rising. This will be linked to exposure to asbestos of more recent origin. It may be some time yet before the major reductions in exposure levels and in the use of crocidolite which took place in the early 1970s show up in the mesothelioma mortality figures.

117 The numbers of awards for mesothelioma have continued to rise steeply in recent years, though they fall well short of the numbers recorded on death certificates (currently well over 800 a year). Although both sources are imperfect, the death certificate series (Table 32) probably gives a more reliable picture of trends in the incidence of this disease than the numbers of Disablement Benefit awards (Table 27), since death certification will not be affected by changes in compensation rules or their application, nor by changes in individuals' propensity to claim compensation.

118 Table 33 gives a breakdown of deaths from mesothelioma by sex and age for eight three-year periods from 1968-70 to 1989-91. The proportion of these deaths that were in males rose from 76% in 1968-70 to 86% in 1989-91, reflecting the higher rate of increase in male deaths over the period. Comparing 1989-91 with 1968-70 there was a 6-fold increase in male deaths whilst female deaths tripled.

119 Comparing the two most recent three year periods, one sees increases in the numbers of male deaths in each age group except the under 45s. For females there were increases in all age groups except the under 45s and those aged 55-64. The number of female deaths doubled in the 45-54 age group.

120 Mesothelioma death rates (per million) are given for Great Britain and the standard regions in Table 34 for the three periods 1983-85, 1986-88 and 1989-91. For both males and females the rates for Great Britain follow an upward trend, reaching 29.4 and 4.6 deaths per million respectively.

121 Death rates for men and women increased across the three periods for all regions except the northern region where the rate fell slightly between 1986-88 and 1989-91. The northern region did however maintain its position as the region with the highest rate for each of the three periods for men, although for women this position has been taken by Greater London in 1989-91. With smaller numbers involved the pattern of female regional rates is however more variable.

122 *Asbestos-related lung cancer* as a prescribed disease has given rise to an average of 56 awards/year over the last six years (see Figure 18). Studies of particular groups of asbestos exposed workers suggest that the numbers of excess lung cancers produced is - roughly, and with considerable variation from study to study - double the number of mesotheliomas[6]. This suggests that the actual number of lung cancer cases attributable to asbestos exposure is currently estimated at about 1800 per year. Many of these cases may not be recognised as such by the sufferers or by their doctors. There is no clinical feature by which lung cancers caused by asbestos can be definitively distinguished from cases in which asbestos has not been involved.

123 *Bilateral diffuse pleural thickening*, prescribed from the same date as lung cancer in asbestos workers, is another disease commonly associated with asbestos exposure, which can lead to impairment of lung function and for which awards of disablement benefit are currently running at about three times the rate recorded for asbestos-related lung cancers.

OTHER OCCUPATIONAL CANCERS

124 For a number of cancers in addition to asbestos-related lung cancer and mesothelioma, a clear occupational link has been established. This has been possible where workplace exposure to a known carcinogen is involved, or where a clear association has been established for example between occurrence of a rare cancer and work in a specific industry or job. In many cases the occupational link has been given recognition in the designation of the cancer as a prescribed disease, for example bladder cancer associated with work exposure to aromatic amines, nasal and lung cancers (nickel) and nasal cancer (in

Figure 18   Occupational cancer other than mesothelioma

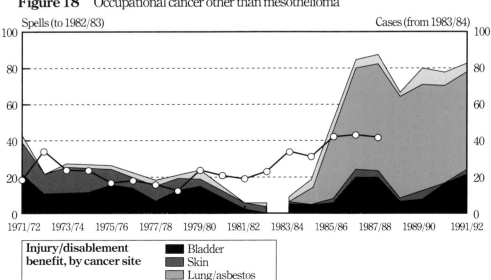

hardwood and leather workers), angiosarcoma of the liver (vinyl chloride), and skin cancer (mineral oil and some other substances). The numbers of awards for these cancers are summarized in Figure 18. As for asbestos-related lung cancers, most cases attributable to these causes are likely to remain undetected and uncompensated.

125 A number of other cancers are thought to be associated with occupational exposures but the identification of a causal link remains the subject of research. Association has been suggested in particular between lung and bladder cancers and a very wide variety of industries and exposures. Confounding with the effects of smoking however makes assessment of the contribution of occupational exposures particularly difficult for these, and especially lung cancer, but they are thought to account for the majority of occupational cancers.

126 No estimate of the total numbers of cancers due to work-related factors can be accurately made, but in a review of the numbers of 'avoidable' cancers, Doll and Peto[7] estimated that around 4% (with a range of acceptable estimates from 2% to 8%) could be avoided by the elimination of all workplace carcinogenic risks (including asbestos exposure); 6.8% of cancer deaths amongst men and 1.25% amongst women. This would imply an annual total of about 5000 premature deaths from work-related cancer in Great Britain amongst men and 900 amongst women. 1.2% of cancers were thought then to be due to asbestos exposure alone.

SURVEILLANCE OF RESPIRATORY DISEASES

127 Since the beginning of 1989, the Epidemiological Research Unit at the London Chest Hospital, in collaboration with the British Thoracic Society and the Society of Occupational Medicine, and funded by HSE, has operated a reporting scheme for cases of occupationally-related respiratory disease seen for the first time by occupational and chest physicians throughout the United Kingdom. This scheme is known as SWORD 'Surveillance of work-related and occupational respiratory disease'. The SWORD team have published detailed analyses of the 1989 data for the full range of respiratory diseases covered, as well as a special study of the asthma cases for 1989 and 1990[8,9]. A summary of the figures for 1989-92 is shown in Table G. It is not straightforward to interpret the figures for this period in terms of time trends because of changes in the diagnostic categories and in the methods of data collection. As from the beginning of 1992, some chest physicians now only send in reports for one month each year, the resulting figures being grossed up by twelve in the annual estimated totals. The remainder of the chest physicians and all the participating occupational physicians form a core group who continue to record all cases. The doubling of the estimated numbers for 1992 compared with previous years is probably a consequence of improved notification from the sampled physicians, for whom the work of reporting is now less onerous. Notification may be more complete in some areas than in others - see the section on asthma below for further discussion. In general it will be the more serious cases that are likely to be seen by a specialist doctor.

Table G Surveillance of work-related and occupational respiratory disease (SWORD) 1989-92

	1989-91 Annual average	*1992* Estimated
Allergic alveolitis	37	97
Asthma	509	1047
Bronchitis	43	133
Building-related illness	15	11
Byssinosis	11	4
Infectious diseases	39	53
Inhalation accidents	193	251
Lung cancer	45	146
Malignant mesothelioma	303	723
Benign pleural disease	313	681
Pneumoconiosis	298	418
Other	41	71
Total	1847	3635

Occupational asthma

128 Summary data for Disablement Benefit for occupational asthma are shown in Figure 19, with detailed figures given in Table 30. Benefit became payable for this condition when linked with a specified range of substances (agents 1 to 7 in the table) from March 1982. From September 1986, seven new categories of sensitizing agents were added to the prescribed list, and a further ten categories were added in September 1991; totals for the original list and for the additional categories are shown separately in the table and in Figure 19. The list now includes an 'open category', under which benefit can be paid for occupational asthma caused by an agent not specifically listed, provided the causal link is proved in each case.

129 Occupational asthma has a much more rapid onset than the pneumoconioses, and awards can be expected to reflect working conditions within a much shorter time-scale. However, the numbers of compensated cases in the early years of prescription may be affected by the spread of knowledge of the possibility of compensation and by the fact that awards can be made retrospectively within ten years of exposure to prescribed conditions.

130 For the original list of agents, the total shows a small but steady increase from an average 162 in the first three full years to 188 in 1990, then rising more sharply to 296 in 1992. The extension of the list of prescribed agents in 1986 produced 49 additional awards in 1987, falling to 28 in 1990, before increasing quite sharply to 72 in 1992. The most recent extension gave rise to 185 additional cases in 1992, 129 of these being in the open category. This category accounted for nearly a quarter of the cases, exceeding any of the individually listed agents. However these high numbers may be a transient effect of the inclusion of existing cases caused by substances which did not previously qualify them for benefit. Excluding these latest additions, five main categories, isocyanates, hardening agents, soldering flux, flour/grain and wood dusts account for nearly all the remaining cases. There was a total of 553 cases in all categories in 1992.

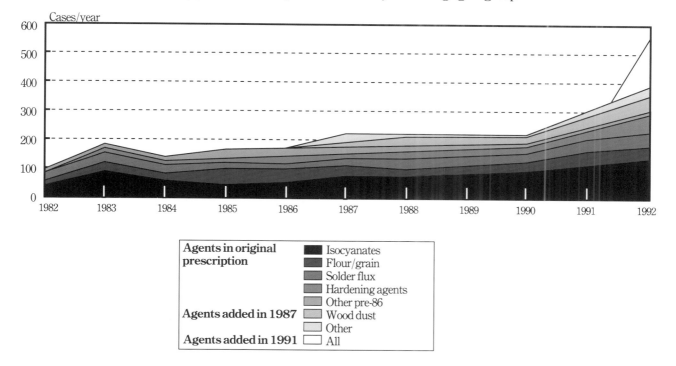

Figure 19 Occupational asthma by sensitising agent group

131 Most cases prior to 1987 (69% overall) were assessed at 13% disability or less, but from 1987 onwards, three-quarters were assessed at 14% or more. In both periods very few were assessed at 50% or more. The pattern of severity is similar for all sensitizing agents. The change in pattern is probably connected with the introduction of the 14% rule. Since overall numbers have continued to rise it is possible that more generous assessment is being given to some borderline cases, and that relatively few are disinclined to apply because their disability may be too slight to qualify.

132 Under the SWORD scheme an average of some 500 new cases of asthma were reported each year from 1989 to 1991. In 1992 the estimated annual number was roughly doubled to 1047, probably as a result of improved reporting arrangements. Analysis of SWORD asthma rates for 1989 showed strong regional variations which were only partly explained by the geographical distribution of industry[8]. If these differences are interpreted as evidence of under-reporting in the SWORD scheme, they imply a national incidence of between one and one-and-a-half times the estimated number obtained under the 1992 arrangements.

133 Only half the cases reported in the SWORD scheme in 1989/90 were due to agents then prescribed[9]. Within this group of cases the pattern of sensitizing agents was broadly similar to that among compensated cases, though isocyanate cases were more dominant among the SWORD cases (44%), than among the compensated cases (33%).

134 The LFS gives an estimate of 68 000 cases of self-reported work-related asthma, of which only 20 000 were thought by the sufferers to be caused rather than merely made worse by work. Supposing on the basis of the SWORD data that there were 1500 new cases each year, 20 000 prevalent cases would represent 13 years' accrued cases. Occupations with above average risk included those in the processing (metal and electrical, and other) groups.

135 Byssinosis is an illness associated with exposure to cotton dust with both acute and, in some cases, long-term effects. The numbers of cases have decreased steadily, although changes in the compensation rules, most recently in 1979, have periodically produced sharp increases in the numbers of compensated cases. The numbers of death certificates with byssinosis recorded as the underlying cause of death (these are only separately identifiable from 1979), have remained constant at around 25 deaths per year (Figure 20 and Table 35). The numbers of byssinosis cases recorded by SWORD fell from 23 in 1989 to four in 1992.

136 Farmer's Lung is an allergic reaction to fungal spores, particularly those which grow in mouldy hay. Similar conditions are suffered by other groups of workers - eg mushroom pickers - with similar exposures. Few cases - around ten per year - are recorded through the compensation system (Figure 21). One explanation for this will be that many farmers are self-employed and therefore cannot claim benefit under the Industrial Injuries Scheme. The numbers of deaths ascribed to Farmer's Lung (and related conditions), is of the same order of magnitude, which suggests, since the disease rarely progresses to a life-threatening level, that there are substantially more cases than those receiving compensation. The SWORD figures show an average of 37 cases of this type of disease (allergic alveolitis) for the three years 1989 to 1991, rising to 97 in 1992 with the improved reporting scheme.

Figure 20   Byssinosis

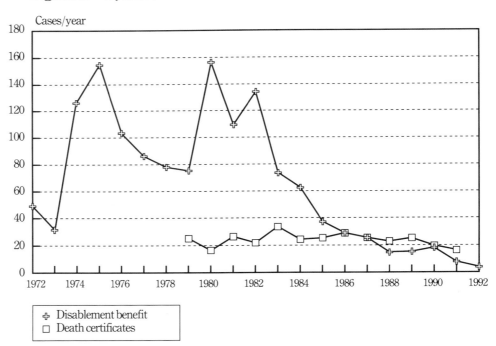

Figure 21 Farmer's Lung

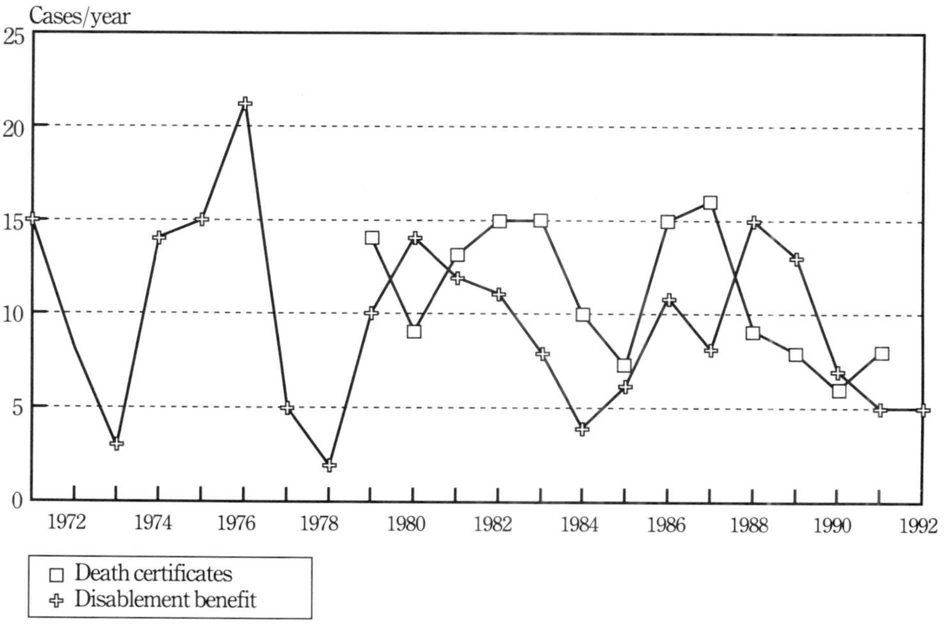

Cases/year

Legend:
□ Death certificates
✛ Disablement benefit

SICK BUILDING SYNDROME

137 The term Sick Building Syndrome refers to a range of relatively minor illnesses which can be caused by the indoor environment. No one specific causative factor has been identified but factors which could be implicated include air-conditioning and humidification systems, poor lighting and air pollution. The usual symptoms reported include nasal problems, eye irritation, dry skin and tiredness. Because these symptoms are common in the general population, and for the most part not serious, they are rarely reported to a doctor and it is very difficult to say with any certainty what the extent of the problem is. Some studies have suggested that between 30 and 50% of buildings could be affected[10]. However, although the symptoms are seldom serious the efficiency loss to an organization in which, perhaps, 20% of their workforce are unnecessarily below par would be considerable. Economic costs could include absenteeism, remedial work on buildings and even, in extreme cases, demolition.

138 Over the period 1989-92 an average of 14 cases of building-related sickness were reported annually to the SWORD register with an additional 190 cases identified from investigations of outbreaks in three buildings. Numbers did not increase in 1992 despite the improved reporting arrangements. Because of the nature of the disease the majority of cases are unlikely to be seen by either an occupational or chest physician, so these figures will certainly underestimate the true incidence. The Labour Force Survey yields an estimate of 2500 people affected in a twelve month period, but this is still likely to be much lower than the true figure, as people may well suffer building-related symptoms without associating them with their working environment.

INFECTIONS

139 There are three main categories of risk group for occupational infections:

(a) A small group of clinical laboratory and research workers exposed to highly dangerous pathogens where even a single infection would represent a failure of adequate control (eg Marburg virus). Cases of infection are very rare.

(b) A much larger group of occupations exposed to higher than normal concentrations of microbiological agents known to cause infections in humans. These include:

(i) Workers whose job brings them in contact with infected humans or human body fluids, such as health workers, laboratory staff and sewage workers. The hazards vary but include hepatitis, tuberculosis, HIV, salmonella and other organisms causing gastroenteritis, etc. Infection is probably under-reported or not recognised as occupational in many cases.

(ii) Workers in contact with animals and animal products, such as farmers, vets, slaughtermen and animal laboratory workers. The hazards are the zoonoses (diseases transmissible from animals to humans) including ringworm, orf, brucellosis, leptospirosis, Q fever and psittacosis. Reporting is seriously incomplete for several reasons. Some diseases are common and easily recognised but are minor, eg ringworm. Some, such as psittacosis, are predominantly non-occupational. Many, such as leptospirosis, cause only influenza-like symptoms in mild cases and the majority are thus never correctly diagnosed. Serological studies of antibodies to leptospira hardjo in farmers, for example, have suggested that there is a considerable burden of mild or sub-clinical disease.

Figure 22   Occupational infections

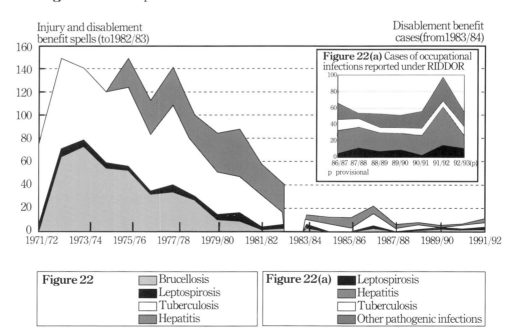

(iii) A diverse group of other workers exposed to pathogenic organisms from plant or environmental sources, such as tetanus from soil and composts, legionellosis in cooling towers, etc. No general source of statistics is available which quantifies these specific problems.

(c) Occupational groups in contact with sections of the public in whom there is a higher than average rate of common infectious diseases will be at increased risk of such infections. For example the 1990 Labour Force Survey suggests that this is likely to be so for teachers and welfare professionals. There is no source from which estimates of the number of occupationally-related cases of such diseases can be obtained.

140 There are few useful sources of statistics on occupational infections. The Communicable Disease Surveillance Centre (CDSC) can provide the best estimates of the overall incidence of infections but at present the proportion attributable to occupation is rarely known. We have previously commented on the CDSC data on a small range of occupational zoonoses but have not continued this practice in the present volume as the data are thought to be misleading. Initiatives are in place to improve the quality of data from this source and it is hoped that the first results will be available next year.

141 Some infections, such as hepatitis, tuberculosis, brucellosis and leptospirosis, are prescribed diseases. However not only will mild cases of brucellosis and leptospirosis go unrecognised but all four infections will rarely lead to disability in the long term and the incidence will not be reflected in payments of disability benefit. Figure 22 and the data in Tables 25 and 26 should therefore be interpreted very cautiously.

DERMATITIS

142 The risk of dermatitis caused by an allergic or irritant reaction to substances used or handled at work is present in a wide range of jobs. However, in the workforce as a whole, the prevalence has fallen as conditions have improved and as the number of 'dirty' jobs has contracted. Figure 23 shows that the annual number of cases of compensated dermatitis

Figure 23   Occupational dermatitis

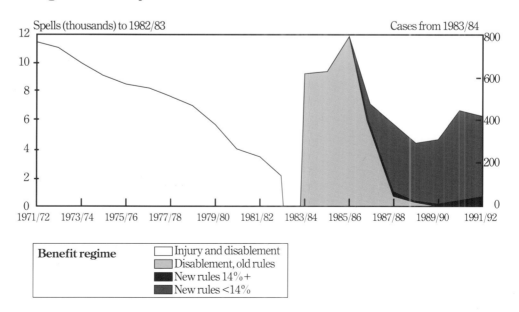

(strictly, the number of spells of sickness absence due to dermatitis for which Industrial Injury Benefit was paid) fell from over 10 000 in 1971/72 to about 2000 in 1982/83 (the 10 months to March 1983, the final period for which Injury Benefit was normally payable). Since then the numbers of disablement benefit cases have fluctuated as the compensation rates have been re-defined; in particular the introduction of the 14% rule is likely to have affected uptake. In the six years since the introduction of this rule, only 82 of the 1839 cases had sufficient disablement from dermatitis to qualify for benefit.

143 There are three other sources for data on occupational dermatitis, two of which are based on records of general practitioner consultations.

144 The *Morbidity Statistics from General Practice* surveys (MSGP) in 1955/56, 1970/71 and 1981/82[11, 12, 13] each give data on consultations for occupational dermatitis, though the definitions used were not exactly the same in all three surveys.

145 In the first six months of 1989, the HSE commissioned a survey based on 73 GPs throughout the UK who recorded the number of cases of occupational dermatitis that they saw in this period. Using this we can estimate that in 1989 there were approximately 38 000 cases of dermatitis caused by work and a further 25 000 cases whose condition was made worse by their work.

146 The 1990 Labour Force Survey yielded estimates of the number of people with dermatitis or other skin diseases which they believed had been caused or made worse by work, these estimates being 54 000 and 30 000 respectively. Over 90% of the cases reported arose as a result of a recent job (in last three years), suggesting that this is not a persistent condition. Among respondents reporting a skin complaint which was caused or made worse by a recent job, three occupations had rates significantly above the average for this complaint: construction, science and engineering, and catering, cleaning and hairdressing. One occupation showed a significantly raised rate in the inactive group (inactive in the last three years): metal and electrical work. This rate was about six times the average rate for the inactive.

147 Figure 24 shows estimates of the annual number of cases of dermatitis, caused or made worse by work, in England and Wales in each of the years where data has been collected: 11 000 in 1955/56, 32 000 in 1970/71, nearly 100 000 in 1981/82, 63 000 in 1989 and 63 000 in 1990. These changes cannot be directly interpreted as trends since the definition of occupational dermatitis was not comparable over all surveys.

148 A surveillance scheme for occupational skin disease (EPIDERM) has been in operation throughout the United Kingdom since February 1993. It follows a pilot reporting scheme for occupational dermatitis which ran for 30 months from August 1990 to January 1993. Consultant dermatologists report to the team at the University of Manchester any new cases of skin disease that they suspect have been caused, or made worse, by work. During the pilot scheme 3557 cases were reported, 3324 with contact dermatitis. In the first three months of the EPIDERM project, 153 dermatologists (50% of UK consultants) reported 659 cases, including 551 of contact dermatitis, 51 of neoplasia associated with occupational skin exposure and 57 for other causes. The most common suspected agents in the first three months of EPIDERM were nickel (16%), rubbers (11%), skin problems associated with wet work (11%), soaps and detergents (10%) and UV radiation (9%). The most common occupations were hairdressers (10%), chefs and cooks (6%), cleaners and

Figure 24   Survey-based estimates of the annual number of cases
of occupational dermatitis

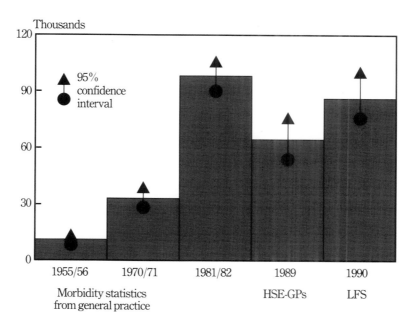

domestics (5%), machine fitters (5%) and nurses (4%). These agents and occupations are similar to those reported for contact dermatitis in the pilot study, which has however documented substantial differences between men and women both in the jobs and agents responsible. Nickel sensitivity is the most common form of problem among women, and exposure to petroleum oils amongst men. Comparison of the frequency of occupation amongst those with skin disease and of occupation as recorded in the Department of Employment's Labour Force Survey showed that hairdressers, florists, printers, machine tool operatives and chemical plant operatives had a risk of dermatitis more than ten times that expected from the frequencies of these occupations in the general population.

149 The EPIDERM project is in its early stages and an unquantified degree of under-reporting may be expected. However the figures to hand suggest that somewhere between 3-5000 new cases of dermatitis caused or made worse by work are recognised each year by consultant dermatologists. This estimate is 10-fold greater than the numbers applying for compensation, but less than one tenth of those estimated from HSE's special labour force enquiry (LFS) to have skin problems due to work. Many skin complaints not seen by dermatologists may be known to occupational physicians, and the EPIDERM reporting scheme will be extended to this group within the coming months.

MUSCULO-SKELETAL DISORDERS

150 Musculo-skeletal conditions affect a very large number of people, both in work and out of it. For example, nearly half of all working age adults will experience some low back pain in any 6-week period. A limited number of specifically work-related musculo-skeletal disorders are prescribed under the II scheme. In the last full year in which injury benefit could be awarded (1981/82) there were 2828 injury and/or disablement benefit cases, and in the last year before restriction of disablement benefit to cases with 14% disability (1985/86) there were 842 disablement benefit cases (Figure 25 and Tables 25 and 26). The GP-

Figure 25 Musculo-skeletal disorders (thousands)

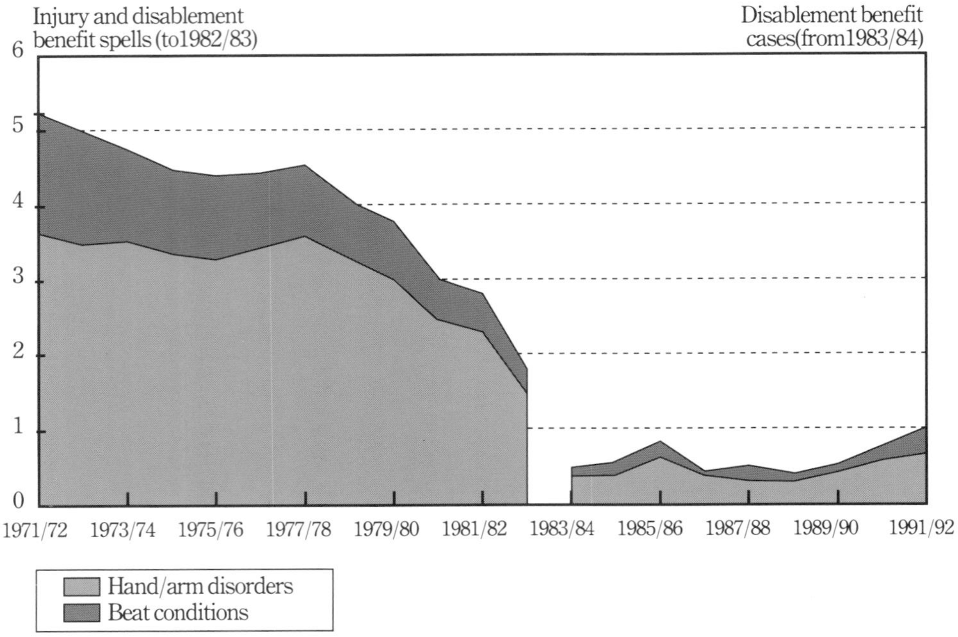

based survey commissioned by HSE in 1989, referred to in the preceding section, also recorded cases of Carpal Tunnel Syndrome (CTS) - symptoms caused by the entrapment or compression of nerves in the wrist - which can be caused by repetitive twisting and gripping. The participating GPs judged that about half of the cases of CTS which they saw were either caused or exacerbated by the patients' work. On this basis the observed rates of work-related CTS were 0.8 per 1000 in women and 0.4 per 1000 in men. This would imply a national annual incidence of 20 000 work-related cases for which medical advice was sought.

151 The LFS trailer results show that musculo-skeletal disorders were the most commonly recorded self-reported work-related illness. The estimated number of prevalent cases 'caused' by work was 593 000 of which 50 000 fell into 'Repetitive Strain Injury' (RSI) category. Over half of the remaining cases recorded back-related problems. The occupations reported as causing or making the RSI condition worse, with significantly raised rates, were repetitive assembly, inspection and packing (mainly female), and construction (all male cases). For general musculo-skeletal disorders (excluding RSI) the highest risk occupation recorded was coal mining, with about 13% of workers affected. This was followed by construction and nursing, each with around 5% affected. Transport, security, processing (metals and electrical), farming, fishing and forestry and 'other' occupations were also significantly above average with rates ranging from 3% to 4.5% of workers affected.

OCCUPATIONAL DEAFNESS

152 Although in recent years the numbers of assessed claims for Disablement Benefit for occupational deafness have been overtaken by those for Vibration White Finger, it remains the second most frequent category in the Prescribed Disease statistics. A change in qualifying conditions was introduced on 1 October 1983; from that date, claimants need only have worked for ten years in prescribed noisy conditions - previously it was 20 years. An earlier widening of the terms of prescription took place in 1979, and the additional claims

Figure 26 Occupational deafness - disablement benefit

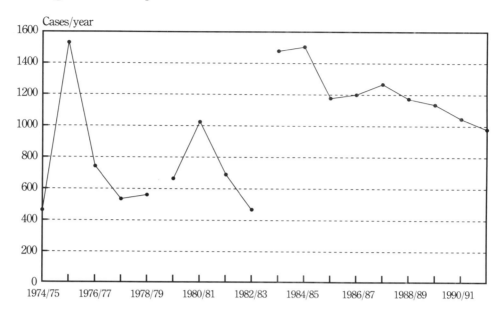

Note: The breaks in the graph indicate changes in prescription rules

due to this reached a peak in 1981. Figures for recent years show a gradual decline from 1261 assessed claims in 1987/88 to 972 in 1991/92. Figure 26 and Table 25 show the annual numbers of new assessed claims. DSS estimate a total of 13 000 people were receiving disablement benefit for occupational deafness in April 1992.

153 Results from population surveys however suggest that the total number of people with occupational deafness may be much larger than the number who receive DSS awards. In the OPCS Disability Survey between 1985 and 1988, deafness was the largest category of 'industrial disease' (described as such by respondents), affecting an estimated 52 500 people in England and Wales.

154 Estimates from the Labour Force Survey are larger still, suggesting that they may include complaints below the threshold of severity set by the OPCS Disability Survey. An estimated 103 100 people in England and Wales had deafness, tinnitus or other ear conditions which they thought had been caused by their work. A further 18 300 thought they had deafness or ear conditions which had been made worse by work.

155 The occupation at highest risk for deafness and ear conditions in the LFS was coal mining, with a risk estimated to be between seven and twenty times the average. The uncertainty attaching to this figure is caused by the difficulty in estimating the population at risk for a condition caused by long-term exposure in an industry where the numbers employed have shrunk very markedly.

156 Other high risk occupations included those in the processing (metal and electrical) group, with over four times the average risk, and the processing (other) group with twice the average risk. Within these groups, jobs such as sheet workers and riveters, and workers in foundries, forging, textile and chemical processing were particularly at risk, reflecting the generally high noise exposures in such jobs.

VIBRATION WHITE FINGER

157 Vibration White Finger (Figure 27 and Table 25) is a disorder of the blood supply to the fingers and hand which can be caused by long-term use of vibrating hand-held tools. The damage caused by vibration is chronic rather than immediate, and recently diagnosed cases will be the product of at least five years' and in some cases more than 20 years' exposure.

Figure 27   Vibration White Finger: disablement benefit cases

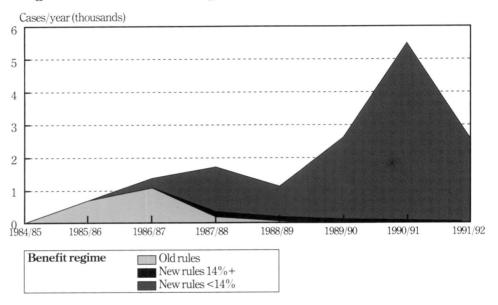

158 Following the prescription of this disease in 1985, numbers of assessed cases rose rapidly, overtaking deafness to reach a peak of 5401 in 1990/91. Numbers fell to 2369 in 1991/92, suggesting the clearance of a backlog of existing cases, but VWF remains the commonest Prescribed Disease.

159 The growth in numbers up to 1990/91 seems' not to have been affected by the 14% disablement rule - only 26 of the 2369 cases in 1991/92 received benefit for VWF alone, although some others may have reached the benefit threshold through aggregation of their VWF disability with that due to another prescribed disease (usually occupational deafness, since vibrating tools can also be very noisy). Also it is believed that compensation agreements between some employers, their insurers and trade unions may have contributed to the increase, since solicitors handling a claim against the employer may also initiate a claim for DSS benefit.

160 The Labour Force Survey yields an estimate of 7300 sufferers from VWF nationally. This number seems low in relation to the DSS figures, since summing the numbers of assessed cases since 1983 gives a minimum prevalence estimate of 15 100 for the more serious cases, (though this is without deductions for any that have subsequently recovered or died). The lowness of the LFS estimate may be partly due to sampling error, and partly to the fact that respondents who reported more than one work-related disorder were asked to specify only the one regarded as more serious (though the total number of disorders was recorded). Because of this those who suffered from both VWF and another work-related disorder such as deafness might report the latter in preference, and the VWF would be

missed by the survey. As noted above, noise and vibration exposures occur together in many jobs. An upper bound estimate of 21 000 can be obtained by assuming that all LFS respondents who reported occupational deafness plus something else also had VWF. Even higher estimates can be obtained by multiplying estimated numbers of workers exposed to hand transmitted vibration [14, 15] by typical prevalence rates obtained from industrial studies. Such a technique is liable however to overestimate the true prevalence since industrial studies tend to concentrate on workplaces where exposures or prevalence are especially high. Combining estimates from various sources suggests a best estimate of around 20 000 cases[16].

ACUTE POISONING

161 Acute poisoning by chemicals at work is reportable under RIDDOR as an industrial accident (and, for some substances, also as a reportable illness). Around 2000 cases are reported annually, with ten to 25 fatalities.

162 A study commissioned by HSE of cases of poisoning by industrial chemicals in 1985 based on a 10% sample of attendances at NHS Accident and Emergency Departments showed that 6% of attendances for poisoning arose from workplace exposures. This implies an annual national total of about 14 000 cases. The commonest categories of substance were acids, alkalis, irritant vapours and solvents. There were no deaths in the sample, and the discharge rate was higher than for other types of poisoning, suggesting a higher proportion of precautionary attendances.

163 Less than 20 deaths from pesticide poisoning are reported to coroners annually in England and Wales and all occur in adults (usually men); most are due to the suicidal ingestion of paraquat.

164 A surveillance study of all acute poisonings from pesticides commissioned by the HSE and conducted by the West Midlands Poison Unit (WMPU) has indicated that at least 5500 suspected pesticide poisoning incidents occur annually in the UK. This figure is based on enquiries made to the seven centres in the National Poisons Information Service network, and covers non-occupational as well as occupational incidents. Of these some 700 patients, including approximately 500 children under ten years, are admitted to hospital with pesticide poisoning, but 95% of children admitted are discharged in less than two days, indicating a low morbidity.

165 Only 18% of the 790 cases of suspected pesticide poisoning reported to the WMPU under the Green Card scheme between June 1991 and May 1993 were 'confirmed' or 'likely' poisonings, as defined according to a system based on that used by the Pesticide Incidents Appraisal Panel (PIAP). Most had mild or moderate symptoms only (60% and 34% respectively, 'moderate' being defined as evidence of organ damage without signs of organ failure). Thirty-one of the 790 cases reported (4%) involved exposure to a sheep dip, with 12 of these classified as 'likely poisonings'.

166 Suspected pesticide poisoning incidents reviewed by PIAP can be differentiated as occupational or non-occupational. Between April 1989 and March 1992 there were 275 pesticide poisoning incidents involving 503 people reported to HSE, of which 237 (involving 359 people) were assessed by PIAP. Of these 60 incidents (involving 74 workers) occurred in an occupational setting. Two-thirds of these had symptoms that 'confirmed' exposure

or were thought 'likely' to be related to pesticide exposure. 36% of all 'confirmed' (occupational and other) cases were working with the pesticide or in close proximity to the operator. However 41% were on adjacent private property and 23% were walking, cycling or jogging past while spraying was taking place.

EXPOSURE TO LEAD

167 The Control of Lead at Work Regulations 1980 require regular medical examination of all workers with significant exposure to lead, by an Appointed Doctor. The examinations include measurement of workers' blood-lead levels. Annual returns from Appointed Doctors give summary statistics for each workplace based on the maximum blood lead level recorded for each worker under surveillance.

Figure 28   Blood lead levels: males

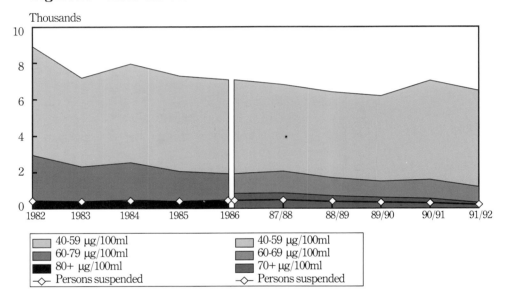

Figure 29   Blood lead levels: females

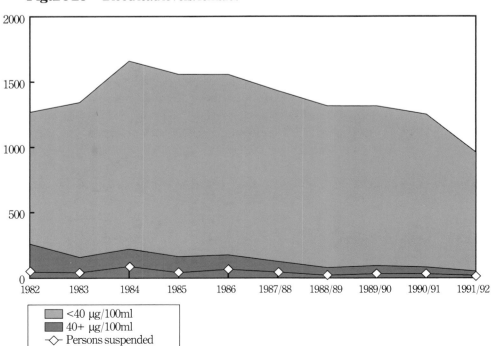

168 Figures 28 and 29 are based on the returns since 1982 and Table 36 refers to the period 1986 to 1991/92. The figures refer to calendar years for 1982 to 1986 and to financial years (April 1 to March 31) from 1987/88 onwards. The regulations prescribe that when a male worker's blood-lead level exceeds a certain limit (79 µg/100 ml from 1982 to 1985 but lowered to 69 µg/100 ml in 1986) the responsible doctor will consider whether he should be suspended from working with lead. For females of reproductive capacity a lower limit of 39 µg/100 ml is prescribed, above which the doctor will consider suspension from work.

169 The number of males under surveillance fell somewhat from 25 400 in 1990/91 to 24 000 in 1991/92, though this total was similar to those recorded for earlier years back to 1985. The number of men with a blood-lead level over 69 µg/100 ml has fallen in four successive years from 762 in 1987/88 to 276 in 1991/92. Numbers in the 60-69 µg/100 ml range have similarly fallen, whilst there have been compensatory increases in the proportions in the lower ranges. Numbers of workers suspended from work fell in line with the fall in numbers with high levels; 55% of those with levels over 69 µg/100 ml were suspended in 1991/92 compared with 58% in the previous year and 51% in 1986. A worker with a high reading need not be suspended if a repeat measurement is below the limit though he would still be recorded on the annual return as being above the limit.

170 The number of females under surveillance has fallen steadily from 1550 in 1985 to 1250 in 1990/91, then more sharply to 960 in 1991/92. Thus the decline of employment in the lead industries in 1991/92 was proportionately more marked in women than in men; a similar difference was seen in the reductions of numbers of women and men employed in manufacturing industries generally. The numbers with blood-lead levels above 39 µg/100 ml fell from 168 (11% of female workers) in 1986 to 52 (5.4% of females) in 1991/92. The numbers of females suspended from work in recent years were small and subject to fluctuations; there were 13 such in 1991/92 compared with 26 the previous year.

171 Table 37 shows the distribution of blood-lead levels by industrial sector in 1991/92. Smelting, refining and casting, the lead battery industry and the manufacture of lead compounds accounted for most of the males under surveillance. The main areas of employment for women were glass making, potteries, glazes and transfers, lead batteries and smelting, refining and casting.

172 The sectors having the highest proportions of men over 69 µg/100 ml were the demolition and scrap industries. However the numbers of men under surveillance in these sectors were relatively small and the numbers of these that had high levels are prone to the fluctuations that affect small counts. In absolute terms the lead battery industry accounted for the greatest number of men over the limit, but this partly reflected the high number who were employed in this sector. Following improvements in hygiene and control, the proportion of men in lead batteries who were over 69 µg/100 ml has fallen from 9.1% in 1988/89 to 2.5% in 1991/92.

173 For women the data are given as numbers rather than percentages since the numbers who exceed the 39 µg/100 ml level were very small. Most of the 52 women who were over this level were employed in lead batteries or in the sector working with metallic lead or alloys.

OCCUPATIONAL EXPOSURE TO IONIZING RADIATION

174 In its most recent report of radiation exposure of the UK population, the National Radiological Protection Board (NRPB) estimated that about 280 000 workers are exposed to ionizing radiations while at work, of which some 120 000 are exposed mainly to natural sources of radiation such as cosmic radiation and the radioactive decay products of radon gas.

175 Employers must make arrangements with approved dosimetry services (ADS) to carry out systematic dose assessments for each of their employees who they have designated as a classified person under the Ionizing Radiations Regulations 1985. In practice, many other workers are also routinely monitored for other reasons.

176 ADS submit annual summaries of doses recorded for classified workers to HSE's Central Index of Dose Information (CIDI), which is operated under contract by NRPB. Statistical summaries of this data have been published for each year from 1986 to 1991. HSE has also published a review of trends in dose information reported to CIDI over the period 1986-91.

177 The statistical summary for 1991 shows that doses were reported for 57 938 in that year with a mean whole-body dose, after standard corrections, of 1 mSv. The corresponding figures for 1986 were 56 044 persons and a mean dose of 2.3 mSv. Over the period 1986-91 there was a more than 10-fold reduction in the number of classified persons with an annual whole-body dose above the principal investigation level of 15 mSv; including 'notional doses' only 164 persons (less than 0.3% of the total) had a reported dose greater than this in 1991.

178 The occupational categories of nuclear reactor operations (6364 persons), nuclear reactor maintenance (9984 persons), nuclear fuel fabrication (3783 persons) and nuclear fuel reprocessing (5423 persons) accounted for nearly 45% of classified persons in 1991. Mean doses for these categories were 1.3 mSv, 1.1 mSv, 1.7 mSv and 1.8 mSv respectively, after correcting for 'notional doses'.

179 The occupational group with the highest average annual dose in 1991 was non-coal mining underground, with an average annual dose of 14.7 mSv, excluding 'notional doses'. Industrial radiography can be hazardous, particularly when carried out on site. 5418 classified persons were employed in this occupation during 1991 with a mean dose of 0.9 mSv, after correcting for 'notional doses'; nearly 1% had annual doses greater than 15 mSv.

**ANNEX I :
STATISTICAL
PUBLICATIONS
AVAILABLE
FROM HSE AND
CONTACTS FOR
ENQUIRIES**

Key fact sheets

1	Back injuries	-	1987/88 - 1990/91
2	Exposure injuries	-	1986/87 - 1989/90
3	Eye injuries	-	1987/88 - 1990/91
4	Falls from a height	-	1986/87 - 1990/91
5	Foot and toe injuries	-	1987/88 - 1989/90
6	Handling injuries	-	1986/87 - 1990/91
7	Machinery injuries	-	1986/87 - 1990/91
8	Slips/trips	-	1986/87 - 1990/91
9	Struck by object/material injuries	-	1986/87 - 1988/89
10	Upper Limb injuries	-	1987/88 - 1989/90
11	Over-3-day injuries caused by fractures, sprains and strains, contusions and lacerations/superficial wounds	-	1986/87 - 1988/89
12	Major injuries caused by fractures or amputations	-	1986/87 - 1988/89
13	Injuries to persons on Youth Training Schemes and to young employees	-	1986/87 - 1990/91
14	Labour Force Survey(LFS)	-	General background information relating to the 1990 trailer to the LFS; together with some key estimated results, eg levels of estimated injury reporting for main industry sectors.

Industry sector profiles

(Include injury, dangerous occurrence and enforcement statistics unless otherwise specified)

Chemicals	-	1981 - 1988/89
Food, drink and tobacco	-	1981 - 1988/89
Mechanical engineering	-	1981 - 1989/90
Motor vehicle manufacturing	-	1981 - 1990/91
Paper, printing, publishing	-	1981 - 1988/89
Textiles	-	1981 - 1988/89
Timber and wooden furniture	-	1981 - 1988/89
Pharmaceuticals (Mini profile - injury statistics only)	-	1989/90 - 1991/92
Rubber (Injury statistics only - no textual commentary)	-	1986/87 - 1989/90p

A full list of all HSE's publications *Publications in Series* can be obtained from the HSE's Public Enquiry Point (see back cover for details).

Enquiry contact points

Enquiries about statistics for injuries arising from work activity, dangerous occurrences, enforcement action and gas safety should be addressed to:

> Statistical Services Unit
> Health and Safety Executive
> Room 512
> Daniel House
> Stanley Precinct
> Bootle
> Merseyside L20 7HE
> Tel: 051 951 4604/4842

Enquiries about occupational ill-health statistics should be addressed to:

> Epidemiology and Medical Statistics Unit
> Health and Safety Executive
> Room 244
> Magdalen House
> Stanley Precinct
> Bootle
> Merseyside L20 3QZ
> Tel: 051 951 4542/4540

Enquiries about Social Security statistics should be addressed to:

Department of Social Security
Central Office
Benton Park Road
Longbenton
Newcastle upon Tyne
NE98 1YX
Tel: 091 213 5000

Enquiries about domestic accident statistics should be addressed to:

Department of Trade and Industry
Room 306
10-18 Victoria Street
London SW1H 0NN
Tel: 071 215 3215

Enquiries about road traffic accident statistics should be addressed to:

Department of Transport
Room 648
Romney House
43 Marsham Street
London SW1P 3PY
Tel: 071 276 8785/8777

Injuries

1   The source of occupational injury data is reports to enforcing authorities made under the Notification of Accidents and Dangerous Occurrences Regulations 1980 (NADOR) for the years 1981 to 1985 and the Reporting of Injuries, Diseases and Dangerous Occurrences Regulations 1985 (RIDDOR) from 1986/87 onwards, when publication of the statistics was changed to a financial year basis.

2   The duty to report injuries rests with 'responsible persons'. In the case of a reportable accident to an employee, this would be the employer. For a self-employed sub-contractor it would be the main employer or contractor. Depending on the type of premises, the report has to be made to one of the Inspectorates in the Health and Safety Executive or to local authorities.

FATAL INJURIES

3   The definition of a fatal injury includes a death occurring up to a year after the accident.

MAJOR INJURIES

4   Statistics on major injuries occurring after April 1986 are based on regulation 3(2) of RIDDOR, which defines the following as major injuries:

(a)   fracture of the skull, spine or pelvis;
(b)   fracture of any bone:
    (i) in the arm or wrist but not in the hand; or
    (ii) in the leg or ankle, but not in the foot;
(c)   amputation of:
    (i) a hand or foot; or
    (ii) a finger, thumb or toe, or any part thereof if the joint or bone is completely severed;
(d)   the loss of sight of an eye, penetrating injury to an eye or chemical or hot metal burn to an eye;
(e)   injury including burns requiring immediate medical treatment, or loss of consciousness, resulting from an electrical shock from any electrical circuit or equipment, whether or not due to direct contact;
(f)   loss of consciousness resulting from lack of oxygen;
(g)   decompression sickness requiring immediate medical treatment (unless 1981 Diving Operations at Work Regulations apply);
(h)   acute illness requiring medical treatment or loss of consciousness resulting from absorption of substance by inhalation, ingestion or through the skin;
(i)   acute illness requiring medical treatment where there is reason to believe that this resulted from exposure to a pathogen or infected material;
(j)   any other injury which results in the person injured being admitted immediately into hospital for more than 24 hours.

OVER-3-DAY INJURIES

5   Under RIDDOR, employers have a duty to report injuries resulting in an absence from normal work for more than three days.

6   Injuries to employees (including trainees), self-employed persons and also members of the public are reportable if they are judged to have arisen from work activity. However, not all accidents to people arising from work activity are reportable under RIDDOR. The statistics exclude:

(a) accidents giving rise to three or fewer days off work;

(b) assaults on staff;

(c) road traffic accidents involving people travelling in the course of their work, which are covered by road traffic legislation;

(d) accidents reportable under separate merchant shipping, civil aviation and air navigation legislation;

(e) accidents to members of the armed forces;

(f) fatal injuries to the self-employed except when they are working at premises under the control of someone else at work;

(g) accidents notified under the Poisonous Substances Regulations 1984, until their repeal;

(h) injuries to passengers travelling on a railway and members of the public injured on railway premises.

Occupational health statistics

7   The figures in the detailed tables derive from four sources:

(a) cases of prescribed disease compensated under the Industrial Injuries Scheme run by the DSS;

(b) cases of industrial disease and poisonings reported under RIDDOR;

(c) death certificates mentioning either asbestosis or mesothelioma, which are copied to the HSE by the Office of Population Censuses and Surveys (OPCS) and the General Register Office for Scotland; and

(d) maximum levels of blood-lead recorded in the course of medical surveillance of lead workers under the 1981 Lead Regulations.

8   Figures in all tables refer to Great Britain (England, Wales and Scotland) unless otherwise stated.

Prescribed diseases - general

9   The Industrial Injuries Scheme compensates workers (or their dependents) injured or killed by an accident at work or suffering from a prescribed disease. The self-employed are not covered by this scheme. Diseases are only 'prescribed' in connection with defined occupations or occupational conditions. For example, tuberculosis is a prescribed disease, but only in respect of individuals whose occupation involves contact with a source of tuberculous infection. Diseases are only prescribed if some occupational cause is well established, and if terms of prescription can be framed in such a way that most cases falling within the terms will be of genuine occupational origin.

10   Where there is a long delay between the cause of a disease and its appearance, it is difficult both to identify and prove occupational causes, and to frame satisfactory terms of prescription. Even when this is done, the numbers of awards will probably understate the disease's incidence, because individuals may be unaware of the possible occupational origin of their disease.

11   Three principal benefits have been payable under the Industrial Injuries Scheme:

(a) *Injury benefit* (until March 1983), a special, higher rate of sickness benefit was payable to people absent from work because of prescribed disease. The abolition of this special rate of benefit from April 1983 means that this information is no longer available.

(b) *Disablement Benefit* is paid in cases where the disease has led to some long-term loss of function;

(c) *Industrial Death Benefit* (up to April 1988) was paid to a worker's dependents where death is caused or materially accelerated by the prescribed disease.

12   The information that can now be drawn from the Industrial Injuries Scheme relates only to cases of prescribed disease leading to some degree of long-term disability. For claims lodged after 1 October 1986, and for all diseases except pneumoconiosis, byssinosis and mesothelioma, benefit is only paid if disablement is assessed at 14% or more.

Disablement benefit (Tables 25-30)

13   The figures for awards of disablement benefit derive from different sources for two groups of the prescribed diseases. Figures for diseases where compensation is assessed by a 'Special Medical Board' (SMB) are compiled on a calendar year basis and have been available for some years (Table 27). Statistics for the other prescribed diseases (Tables 25 and 26), with the exception of occupational deafness, are currently compiled for years starting on 1 October and have been available on this basis since October 1983, when statistical record keeping was re-organised within the DSS following the abolition of Industrial Injury Benefit. Before this date figures for total awards of disablement benefit for these prescribed diseases were not counted separately from awards of injury benefit.

14   For occupational deafness injury benefit has never been payable so that the statistical basis for this disease was not affected. Figures for occupational deafness in Tables 25 and 26 are quoted for calendar years, that is January to December, not October (of the previous year) to September as is the case for the other prescribed diseases in these tables. Figures

presented this year have been revised for the years prior to 1990 to exclude unsuccessful appeals and references to Medical Appeal Tribunals which had been included in error in previously published statistics. Medical Appeal Tribunal decisions where diagnosis was allowed on appeal are (and always have been) included in the figures.

15   The totals for pneumoconiosis and byssinosis awards are shown for completeness in Table 27; more detailed information on these diseases is given in Tables 28 and 29.

Industrial Death Benefit

16   As noted earlier, Industrial Death Benefit has not been payable to new claimants since 10 April 1988, and the last full year for which award figures are available is 1987. Although there can be considerable delays between a death occurring, a claim being lodged and an award being centrally notified, no new awards of the benefit have come through in the statistics relating to deaths up to 1987. The Industrial Death Benefit table published last year in *Health and Safety Statistics 1990/91*[3] (Table 50) will not therefore be updated further, and has been dropped this year.

17   Data on Death Benefit awards for pneumoconiosis excluding asbestosis, asbestosis and mesothelioma are used in Figures 15, 16 and 17 in the text. Awards are counted in the actual year of death from 1983 onwards. However for years prior to 1983, notifications delayed beyond the year following the year of death were allocated to the year prior to the year of notification, rather than to the year of death, with the proportion of these late notifications varying from year to year.

Industrial disease reported under RIDDOR

18   Table 31 shows the numbers of reports of occupational disease received under RIDDOR. These regulations require employers to report all cases of a defined list of diseases occurring among their employees where :

(a) they receive a doctor's written diagnosis; and

(b) the affected employee's current job involves the work activity specifically associated with the disease.

19   The diseases and their associated occupational conditions are listed in Schedule 2 to the Regulations. The schedule is very largely derived from the DSS Prescribed Diseases List, though with some omissions - notably six of the most common diseases: occupational deafness, dermatitis, tenosynovitis, and the 'beat' conditions. Most of the RIDDOR disease categories can be related to a corresponding DSS prescribed disease in Tables 25, 26 or 27. Comparison of these figures suggests substantial under-reporting under RIDDOR, particularly for diseases with long induction periods (for example, the pneumoconioses and occupational cancers).

Asbestosis and mesothelioma recorded on death certificates (Tables 32-34)

20   The figures in Table 32 are derived from information recorded on death certificates. They show the numbers of death certificates issued each year on which either asbestosis or mesothelioma (or both) are mentioned. Some death certificates mentioning both

conditions do so in ways which suggest that the word 'asbestosis' or mesothelioma, rather than the existence of an asbestos-induced lung fibrosis, which is what the word should strictly mean. Consequently the trends in deaths from asbestosis per se are probably better reflected by the figures for asbestosis without mention of mesothelioma, rather than the total of certificates mentioning asbestosis.

Other deaths from occupational lung disease

21 Deaths from pneumoconiosis, byssinosis and Farmer's Lung, recorded on death certificates as the underlying cause of death and obtained from mortality data supplied by OPCS and the General Register Office for Scotland, are displayed in Table 35 and in Figures 15, 20 and 21 of the text.

ANNEX III:
TABLES

Table 1 Injuries by industry and severity of injury 1992/93p
As reported to all enforcement authorities

		Employees (including trainees)				All reported injuries	
Standard Industrial Classification (SIC 80)		Fatal injuries	Non-fatal major injuries	Fatal and major injuries: rate per 100 000 employees	Over-3-day injuries	Number	Rate per 100 000
Agriculture, forestry and fishing (a)	0	18	414	169.4	1398	1830	717.6
Agriculture and horticulture	01	16	384	166.3	1247	1647	684.5
Forestry	02	2	24	337.6	130	156	2026.0
Fishing (a)	03	–	6	n/a	21	27	n/a
Energy and water supply industries (b)	1	19	745	198.9	6215	6979	1816.5
Coal extraction and manufacture of solid fuels:	11	8	371	662.6	1871	2250	3933.6
of which: Coal mines	1113	7	332	650.7	1723	2062	3957.8
Open cast coal workings	1114	1	37	904.8	136	174	4142.9
Coke ovens	12	–	2	285.7	37	39	5571.4
Extraction of mineral oil and natural gas (b)	13	4	77	162.0	517	598	1196.0
Mineral oil processing	14	–	17	100.0	98	115	676.5
Nuclear fuel production	15	–	15	99.3	136	151	1000.0
Production and distribution of electricity, gas and other forms of energy	16	7	199	106.2	2768	2974	1533.8
Water supply industry	17	–	64	127.2	788	852	1693.8
Extraction of minerals and ores other than fuels; manufacture of metals, mineral products and chemicals	2	22	1012	171.1	8416	9450	1563.3
Extraction and preparation of metalliferous ores and extraction of minerals not elsewhere specified	21/23	7	101	435.5	583	691	2786.3
Metal manufacturing	22	–	276	219.6	2230	2506	1993.6
Manufacture of non-metallic mineral products	24	7	282	186.1	2555	2844	1831.3
Chemical industry	25	8	341	119.0	2979	3328	1134.3
Production of man-made fibres	26	–	12	222.2	69	81	1500.0
Metal goods, engineering and vehicles industries	3	23	1878	99.7	16 166	18 067	947.4
Manufacture of metal goods not elsewhere specified	31	6	489	192.2	3657	4152	1611.8
Mechanical engineering	32	11	545	88.5	4317	4873	775.3
Manufacture of office machinery and data processing equipment	33	–	34	51.6	180	214	324.7
Electrical and electronic engineering	34	2	284	62.0	2443	2729	591.7
Manufacture of motor vehicles and parts thereof	35	2	264	118.5	3186	3452	1538.3
Manufacture of other transport equipment	36	2	234	127.9	2095	2331	1263.4
Instrument engineering	37	–	28	32.9	288	316	371.3
Other manufacturing industries	4	13	2393	135.9	22 727	25 133	1419.2
Food, drink and tobacco manufacturing industries	41/42	7	1052	219.7	12 278	13 337	2767.0
Textile industries	43	–	178	105.7	1411	1589	943.6
Manufacture of leather or leather goods	44	–	10	64.1	121	131	839.7
Footwear and clothing industries	45	–	80	37.5	670	750	351.9
Timber and wooden furniture industries	46	2	370	200.8	1995	2367	1277.4
Manufacture of paper and paper products, printing and publishing	47	2	347	77.6	3088	3437	764.0
Processing of rubber and plastics	48	2	319	168.2	2840	3161	1655.8

	Self-employed				Members of the public			Total		
Fatal injuries	Non-fatal major injuries	Over-3-day injuries	All reported injuries		Fatal injuries	Non-fatal major injuries		Fatal injuries	Non-fatal major injuries	Over-3-day injuries	All reported injuries
19	105	123	247		12	48		49	567	1521	2137
14	81	91	186		12	45		42	510	1338	1890
4	23	32	59		–	2		6	49	162	217
1	1	–	2		–	1		1	8	21	30
1	11	25	37		2	26		22	782	6240	7044
1	8	23	32		–	4		9	383	1894	2286
1	5	23	29		–	2		8	339	1746	2093
–	3	–	3		–	1		1	41	136	178
–	–	–	–		–	–		–	2	37	39
–	–	–	–		–	–		4	77	517	598
–	–	–	–		–	–		–	17	98	115
–	1	–	1		–	1		–	17	136	153
–	–	1	1		1	16		8	215	2769	2992
–	2	1	3		1	5		1	71	789	861
–	35	46	81		–	12		22	1059	8462	9543
–	8	11	19		–	2		7	111	594	712
–	5	4	9		–	–		–	281	2234	2515
–	12	16	28		–	4		7	298	2571	2876
–	10	14	24		–	6		8	357	2993	3358
–	–	1	1		–	–		–	12	70	82
1	44	51	96		–	18		24	1940	16 217	18 181
–	16	11	27		–	1		6	506	3668	4180
1	11	28	40		–	11		12	567	4345	4924
–	–	1	1		–	2		–	36	181	217
–	10	8	18		–	–		2	294	2451	2747
–	5	1	6		–	–		2	269	3187	3458
–	2	2	4		–	3		2	239	2097	2338
–	–	–	–		–	1		–	29	288	317
1	48	76	125		–	19		14	2460	22 803	25 277
–	14	30	44		–	4		7	1070	12 308	13 385
–	–	–	–		–	–		–	178	1411	1589
–	–	–	–		–	–		–	10	121	131
–	2	1	3		–	–		–	82	671	753
1	20	29	50		–	6		3	396	2024	2423
–	5	5	10		–	2		2	354	3093	3449
–	6	8	14		–	2		2	327	2848	3177

Notes
(a) Excludes sea fishing.   (b) Includes the number of injuries in the oil and gas industry collected under offshore installations safety legislation.
(c) Injuries arising from shore based services only. Excludes incidents reported under merchant shipping legislation.
n/a not available   p provisional

Table 1 cont'd Injuries by industry and severity of injury 1992/93p
As reported to all enforcement thorities

		Employees (including trainees)				All reported injuries	
		Fatal injuries	Non-fatal major injuries	Fatal and major injuries: rate per 100 000 employees	Over-3-day injuries	Number	Rate per 100 0
Other manufacturing industries	49	–	37	56.2	324	361	548.
Total manufacturing industries	2-4	58	5283	124.7	47 309	52 650	1229.
Construction	5	63	2062	246.8	11 675	13 800	1602
Distribution, hotels and catering; repairs	6	15	2093	47.0	15 159	17 267	384.
Wholesale distribution (including dealing in scrap and waste materials)	61/62	9	388	46.5	2170	2637	300.
Commission agents	63	–	1	3.0	11	12	35.
Retail distribution	64/65	–	899	39.8	8265	9164	405.
Hotels and catering	66	3	418	36.1	2204	2625	225.
Repair of consumer goods and vehicles	67	3	387	221.5	2509	2899	1646.
Transport and communication (c)	7	39	1311	106.3	15 531	16 881	1329.
Railways	71	11	326	251.7	3883	4220	3151.
Other inland transport	72	15	327	87.1	3145	3487	888.
Sea transport (c)	74	4	4	25.8	27	35	112.
Air transport	75	2	41	64.8	423	466	701.
Supporting services to transport	76	4	117	165.8	993	1114	1526.
Miscellaneous transport services and storage not elsewhere specified	77	2	101	53.7	935	1038	541.
Postal services and telecommunications	79	1	395	103.8	6125	6521	1709.
Banking, finance, insurance, business services and leasing	8	6	266	10.6	1501	1773	69.
Banking and finance	81	–	63	10.9	381	444	76.
Insurance, except for compulsory social security	82	–	16	6.3	131	147	58.
Business services	83	2	113	7.9	619	734	50.
Renting of moveables	84	4	61	56.0	196	261	225.
Owning and dealing in real estate	85	–	13	7.9	174	187	113.
Other services	9	31	4056	59.6	37 753	41 840	609.
Public administration, national defence, compulsory social security and sanitary services	91/92	23	1496	83.9	18 118	19 637	1085.
Education	93	1	1164	64.2	4858	6023	332.
Research and development	94	–	65	75.1	335	400	462.
Medical and other health services, veterinary services	95	1	752	48.4	10 046	10 799	693.
Other services provided to general public	96	–	267	29.3	2629	2896	317.
Recreational services and other cultural services	97	5	274	56.6	1403	1682	341.
Personal services	98	1	38	20.5	364	403	211.
Domestic services	99	–	–	–	–	–	
Total service industries	6-9	91	7726	51.5	69 944	77 761	512.
Unclassified		–	296	n/a	1726	2022	n/
All industries		249	16 526	80.0	138 267	155 042	739.

Self-employed				Members of the public		Total			
Fatal injuries	Non-fatal major injuries	Over-3-day injuries	All reported injuries	Fatal injuries	Non-fatal major injuries	Fatal injuries	Non-fatal major injuries	Over-3-day injuries	All reported injuries
–	1	3	4	–	5	–	43	327	370
2	127	173	302	–	49	60	5459	47 482	53 001
24	678	1278	1980	5	100	92	2840	12 953	15 885
6	24	44	74	13	1299	34	3416	15 203	18 653
2	10	13	25	1	15	12	413	2183	2608
–	–	–	–	–	–	–	1	11	12
1	5	10	16	3	808	4	1712	8275	9991
–	3	7	10	9	471	12	892	2211	3115
3	6	14	23	–	5	6	398	2523	2927
2	13	12	27	3	34	44	1358	15 543	16 945
–	–	–	–	–	–	11	326	3883	4220
2	5	5	12	1	5	18	337	3150	3505
–	–	–	–	–	–	4	4	27	35
–	1	1	2	–	3	2	45	424	471
–	3	4	7	2	20	6	140	997	1143
–	–	1	1	–	–	2	101	936	1039
–	4	1	5	–	6	1	405	6126	6532
–	8	13	21	3	82	9	356	1514	1879
–	1	3	4	–	16	–	80	384	464
–	–	1	1	–	–	–	16	132	148
–	2	6	8	3	56	5	171	625	801
–	5	3	8	–	2	4	68	199	271
–	–	–	–	–	8	–	21	174	195
6	83	384	473	83	8663	120	12 802	38 137	51 059
3	43	321	367	16	666	42	2205	18 439	20 686
–	7	11	18	3	4788	4	5959	4869	10 832
–	–	3	3	–	1	n/a	66	338	404
–	4	6	10	21	895	22	1651	10 052	11 725
–	2	4	6	31	1067	31	1336	2633	4000
2	27	38	67	12	1243	19	1544	1441	3004
–	–	1	1	–	3	1	41	365	407
1	–	–	1	–	–	1	–	–	1
14	128	453	595	102	10 078	207	17 932	70 397	88 536
–	41	46	87	–	101	–	438	1772	2210
60	1090	2098	3248	121	10 402	430	28 018	140 365	168 813

Notes
(a) Excludes sea fishing.
(b) Includes the number of injuries in the oil and gas industry collected under offshore installations safety legislation.
(c) Injuries arising from shore based services only. Excludes incidents reported under merchant shipping legislation.
n/a not available   p provisional

Table 2 Fatal injuries reported to enforcement authorities by industry 1981 - 1992/93p

Standard Industrial Classification (1980)		Agriculture forestry and fishing (b)	Energy and water supply industries (c)(d)(e)	Total manu-facturing industries (d)	Construction	Service industries (f)	Unclassified	All industries
	Division	0	1	2-4	5	6-9		
EMPLOYMENT STATUS	YEAR (a)							
Injury numbers :	1981	31	54	123	105	102	26	441
	1982	27	77	137	100	117	14	472
	1983	29	48	118	118	111	24	448
	1984	29	48	142	100	105	14	438
	1985	20	46	124	104	99	7	400
EMPLOYEES	1986/87	27	30	109	99	80	10	355
	1987/88	21	33	99	103	96	9	361
	1988/89	21	203 (g)	94	101	109	1	529 (g)
	1989/90	23	31	108	100	108	–	370
	1990/91	25	27	88	96	110	–	346
	1991/92	18	31	68	83	97	–	297
	1992/93p	18	19	58	63	91	–	249
	1981	26	–	6	11	10	1	54
	1982	22	–	2	18	6	–	48
	1983	26	1	9	22	7	–	65
	1984	25	–	5	17	13	–	60
SELF-EMPLOYED	1985	44	–	–	22	5	–	71
	1986/87	17	–	1	26	8	–	52
	1987/88	31	–	5	40	8	–	84
	1988/89	25	2	7	36	10	–	80
	1989/90	30	–	7	54	14	–	105
	1990/91	27	–	10	28	22	–	87
	1991/92	32	1	8	16	14	–	71
	1992/93p	19	1	2	24	14	–	60
	1981	13	3	5	12	38	–	71
	1982	17	1	5	13	47	–	83
	1983	9	6	7	11	52	–	85
	1984	7	23	3	7	61	4	105
MEMBERS OF	1985	11	17	5	13	110 (h)	3	159 (h)
THE PUBLIC	1986/87	16	7	5	14	43	7	92
	1987/88	10	2	–	15	82	4	113
	1988/89	15	2	4	14	84	2	121
	1989/90	12	4	3	11	176(i)	–	206(i)
	1990/91	15	3	4	9	108	–	139
	1991/92	5	2	2	6	90	–	105
	1992/93p	12	2	–	5	102	–	121

	Division	Agriculture forestry and fishing (b)	Energy and water supply industries (c) (d) (e)	Total manu-facturing industries (d)	Construction	Service industries (f)	Unclassified	All industries
Incidence rates: (per 100 000)	YEAR (a)	0	1	2-4	5	6-9		
	1981	8.8	7.8	2.0	9.7	0.8	n/a	2.1
	1982	7.8	11.5	2.4	9.7	0.9	n/a	2.3
	1983	8.6	7.5	2.2	11.6	0.8	n/a	2.2
	1984	8.8	7.9	2.7	9.8	0.8	n/a	2.1
	1985	6.1	8.0	2.4	10.5	0.7	n/a	1.9
EMPLOYEES	1986/87	8.6	5.8	2.1	10.2	0.6	n/a	1.7
	1987/88	6.8	6.7	1.9	10.3	0.7	n/a	1.7
	1988/89	7.0	42.7(g)	1.8	9.9	0.7	n/a	2.4(g)
	1989/90	8.1	6.9	2.1	9.4	0.7	n/a	1.7
	1990/91	9.0	6.1	1.8	9.3	0.7	n/a	1.6
	1991/92	6.7	7.4	1.5	8.8	0.6	n/a	1.4
	1992/93p	7.1	4.9	1.4	7.3	0.6	n/a	1.2
	1981	10.4	n/a	4.1	2.8	0.8	n/a	2.6
	1982	8.9	n/a	1.4	4.5	0.5	n/a	2.3
	1983	10.6	n/a	6.0	5.4	0.5	n/a	3.0
	1984	10.0	n/a	2.8	3.7	0.8	n/a	2.5
	1985	17.7	n/a	–	4.7	0.3	n/a	2.8
SELF-EMPLOYED	1986/87	6.9	n/a	0.5	5.3	0.5	n/a	2.0
	1987/88	12.7	n/a	2.0	7.4	0.5	n/a	3.0
	1988/89	10.3	n/a	2.7	6.1	0.5	n/a	2.7
	1989/90	12.3	n/a	2.5	7.5	0.7	n/a	3.3
	1990/91	10.9	n/a	3.7	3.9	1.1	n/a	2.7
	1991/92	13.0	n/a	2.8	2.5	0.7	n/a	2.3
	1992/93p	6.9	n/a	0.6	3.7	0.8	n/a	1.9

Notes

(a) 1981-85 calendar years - reported under the Notification of Accidents and Dangerous Occurrences Regulations (NADOR) 1980. 1986/87 onwards years commencing 1 April - reported under the Reporting of Injuries, Diseases and Dangerous Occurrences Regulations (RIDDOR) 1985.

(b) Excludes sea fishing.

(c) Includes the number of injuries in the offshore oil and gas industry collected under offshore safety legislation.

(d) Fatal injuries to the self-employed and members of the public reported to the Mines and Quarries Inspectorate for the years 1981 to 1984 are included with injuries reported to employees.

(e) Due to the small number of self-employed workers in this sector, the calculation of injury incidence rates would not be reliable.

(f) Fatal injuries to the self-employed reported to local authorities for the years 1981-1985 are included with injuries reported to employees.

(g) Data includes the 167 fatalities of the Piper Alpha disaster, 6 July 1988.

(h) Data includes the 56 fatalities to members of the public in the Bradford City Football Club fire disaster.

(i) Data includes the 95 fatalities to members of the public in the Hillsborough disaster, 15 April 1989.

p   provisional

n/a not available

Table 3 Non-fatal major injuries reported to enforcement authorities by industry 1986/87 - 1992/93p

Standard Industrial Classification (1980)	Agriculture forestry and fishing (a)	Energy and water supply industries (b) (c)	Total manu-facturing industries	Construction	Service industries	Unclassified	All industries
Division	0	1	2-4	5	6-9		

EMPLOYMENT STATUS	YEAR							
Injury numbers	1986/87	429	1718	7378	2736	8057	377	20 695
	1987/88	498	1397	7233	2767	7936	226	20 057
	1988/89	451	1262	7380	2907	7810	134	19 994
EMPLOYEES	1989/90	403	1140	7365	3180	8189	119	20 396
	1990/91	443	1061	6794	2907	8514	177	19 896
	1991/92	404	935	5827	2570	7640	221	17 597
	1992/93p	414	745	5283	2062	7726	296	16 526
	1986/87	72	5	89	443	80	1	690
	1987/88	91	6	100	561	105	4	867
	1988/89	132	5	134	753	124	4	1152
SELF-EMPLOYED	1989/90	102	6	132	927	138	5	1310
	1990/91	115	13	129	931	119	19	1326
	1991/92	77	11	131	729	125	28	1101
	1992/93p	105	11	127	678	128	41	1090
	1986/87	58	30	65	162	14 214	46	14 575
	1987/88	59	17	57	153	12 390	204	12 880
	1988/89	89	29	57	132	12 123	184	12 614
MEMBERS OF THE PUBLIC	1989/90	65	16	24	113	11 119	41	11 378
	1990/91	50	22	39	123	9699	48	9981
	1991/92	54	12	34	148	10 705	56	11 009
	1992/93p	48	26	49	100	10 078	101	10 402
Incidence rates (per 100 000)	1986/87	136.5	330.3	145.0	282.7	57.5	n/a	99.1
	1987/88	162.0	281.9	142.0	276.5	54.9	n/a	94.0
EMPLOYEES	1988/89	151.3	265.6	143.7	285.9	52.5	n/a	91.4
	1989/90	141.9	253.2	144.4	298.8	53.4	n/a	91.8
	1990/91	160.3	239.9	136.1	281.5	55.3	n/a	89.9
	1991/92	150.0	223.2	128.8	272.4	49.7	n/a	81.7
	1992/93p	162.4	193.9	123.5	239.5	50.9	n/a	78.8
	1986/87	29.0	n/a	42.6	91.0	4.9	n/a	26.9
	1987/88	37.1	n/a	40.7	103.5	5.9	n/a	31.0
	1988/89	54.3	n/a	52.1	127.0	6.8	n/a	39.4
SELF-EMPLOYED	1989/90	42.0	n/a	47.1	128.4	7.1	n/a	41.2
	1990/91	46.6	n/a	47.6	129.7	6.0	n/a	41.2
	1991/92	31.2	n/a	45.2	112.5	6.7	n/a	35.9
	1992/93p	38.2	n/a	36.9	104.8	7.1	n/a	35.3

Table 4 Over-3-day injuries reported to enforcement authorities analysed by industry 1986/87 - 1992/93p

Standard Industrial Classification (1980)		Agriculture forestry and fishing (a)	Energy and water supply industries (b) (c)	Total manu-facturing industries	Construction	Service industries	Unclassified	All industries
	Division	0	1	2-4	5	6-9		
EMPLOYMENT STATUS	YEAR							
Injury numbers	1986/87	1043	19 621 (d)	54 046 (d)	16 468	65 958	1875	159 011
	1987/88	1349	15 798	52 734	16 622	69 085	4264	159 852
	1988/89	1473	13 728	56 141	16 597	71 268	3912	163 119
EMPLOYEES	1989/90	1496	11 684	60 006	17 177	74 405	476	165 244
	1990/91	1318	10 256	56 403	16 689	75 344	801	160 811
	1991/92	1423	8232	52 420	14 989	74 219	1223	152 506
	1992/93p	1398	6215	47 309	11 675	69 944	1726	138 267
	1986/87	108	8	99	704	104	6	1029
	1987/88	117	10	122	763	156	1	1159
	1988/89	142	10	128	969	245	9	1503
SELF-EMPLOYED	1989/90	130	21	148	1310	251	5	1865
	1990/91	104	20	146	1554	226	27	2077
	1991/92	118	43	160	1231	232	48	1832
	1992/93p	123	25	173	1278	453	46	2098
Incidence rates (per 100 000)	1986/87	331.7	3771.8	1061.9	1701.8	471.1	n/a	761.1
	1987/88	438.7	3188.3	1035.5	1660.9	478.1	n/a	748.9
EMPLOYEES	1988/89	494.1	2889.5	1093.1	1632.3	478.6	n/a	747.7
	1989/90	526.8	2595.3	1176.5	1614.2	485.4	n/a	743.4
	1990/91	477.0	2318.8	1130.3	1616.2	489.5	n/a	726.5
	1991/92	528.2	1965.1	1158.3	1588.7	482.9	n/a	708.5
	1992/93p	548.2	1617.6	1104.7	1356.0	460.7	n/a	659.5
	1986/87	43.5	n/a	47.4	144.6	6.4	n/a	40.1
	1987/88	47.8	n/a	45.5	140.8	8.8	n/a	41.4
	1988/89	58.4	n/a	49.8	163.4	13.4	n/a	51.4
SELF-EMPLOYED	1989/90	53.3	n/a	52.9	181.4	13.0	n/a	58.6
	1990/91	42.1	n/a	53.9	216.4	11.4	n/a	64.5
	1991/92	47.8	n/a	55.2	190.0	12.4	n/a	59.8
	1992/93p	44.8	n/a	50.3	197.5	25.0	n/a	67.9

Notes (for Tables 3 and 4)
(a) Excludes sea fishing.
(b) Includes the number of injuries in the offshore oil and gas industry collected under offshore safety legislation.
(c) Due to the small number of self-employed workers in this sector, the calculation of injury incidence rates would not be reliable.
(d) Excludes over-3-day injuries reported to the Mines and Quarries Inspectorate for non-British coal mines and for other mining and quarrying activities: figures not readily available.

p   provisional
n/a   not available

Table 5 Injuries to employees by kind of accident and severity of injury 1986/87 - 1992/93p
As reported to all enforcing authorities (a)

Kind of accident	Fatal						
	1986/87	*1987/88*	*1988/89*	*1989/90*	*1990/91*	*1991/92*	*1992/93p*
Contact with moving machinery	34	18	30	25	29	19	21
Struck by moving including flying/falling object	31	53	46	62	51	33	32
Struck by moving vehicle	49	55	70	50	53	52	41
Strike against something fixed or stationary	–	1	3	2	3	3	1
Injured while handling, lifting or carrying	–	2	–	2	–	2	–
Slip, trip or fall on same level	5	5	8	5	1	2	4
Fall from height	84	78	93	110	81	83	56
of which: Up to and including 2 m	9	5	10	13	8	11	10
Over 2 m	69	67	77	89	66	59	41
Height not stated	6	6	6	8	7	13	5
Trapped by something collapsing/overturning	38	34	28	36	24	25	24
Drowning or asphyxiation	19	15	16	15	10	12	7
Exposure to or contact with harmful substance	6	11	8	9	14	2	6
Exposure to fire	3	12	2	8	5	6	7
Exposure to an explosion	8	7	7	8	8	11	5
Contact with electricity or electrical discharge	23	20	18	24	24	14	23
Injured by an animal	–	–	3	–	3	–	2
Other kind of accident	9	33	24	12	28	20	19
Injuries not classified by kind	46	17	173(b)	2	12	13	1
Total	355	361	529	370	346	297	249

			Non-fatal major								Over-3-day			
1986/87	1987/88	1988/89	1989/90	1990/91	1991/92	1992/93p	1986/87	1987/88	1988/89	1989/90	1990/91	1991/92	1992/93p
1948	1990	2118	2003	1738	1472	1332	7066	7470	7968	7848	7724	6983	6190
2444	2800	2541	2752	2371	2157	1967	22 594	24 608	25 076	25 662	23 366	21 927	19 310
635	763	747	772	733	578	545	3182	3519	4254	4146	3845	3792	3304
867	787	808	763	781	642	599	10 797	10 522	10 811	10 886	10 290	9666	8720
1308	1374	1408	1359	1257	1098	1071	48 609	52 320	53 373	55 513	54 220	53 109	48 519
5480	5452	5563	5852	6396	5628	5369	27 836	29 336	30 311	32 087	33 452	31 082	27 845
4058	4234	4340	4551	4274	3994	3649	12 466	13 122	12 516	13 077	12 585	11 749	11 003
1883	1920	1958	2060	1964	1911	1741	7346	7680	7272	7401	7289	6827	6196
1395	1338	1447	1532	1337	1192	991	2081	1805	1786	1918	1759	1450	1386
780	976	935	959	973	891	917	3039	3637	3458	3758	3537	3472	3421
212	246	247	220	204	191	178	591	615	608	616	548	485	459
32	29	28	19	22	28	29	34	38	39	39	26	52	29
979	771	702	804	806	726	724	3724	4015	4123	4586	4516	4180	3673
127	120	106	109	109	75	88	564	552	536	631	576	519	485
100	80	80	74	90	63	48	221	267	231	256	220	233	163
353	331	276	305	298	308	286	551	562	635	703	607	609	591
70	80	75	75	72	66	76	598	723	758	913	853	786	714
499	821	812	657	651	535	545	6516	8080	7880	7562	7281	7166	7118
1583	179	93	81	94	36	20	13 662	4103	4000	719	702	168	144
20 695	20 057	19 944	20 396	19 896	17 597	16 526	159 011	159 852	163 119	165 244	160 811	152 506	138 267

Notes
(a) Includes injuries in the offshore oil and gas industry collected under offshore legislation.
(b) Data include the 167 fatalities of the Piper Alpha disaster, 6 July 1988.
p   provisional

Table 6 Injuries to the self-employed by kind of accident and severity of injury 1986/87 - 1992/93p
As reported to all enforcing authorities

				Fatal			
Kind of accident	*1986/87*	*1987/88*	*1988/89*	*1989/90*	*1990/91*	*1991/92*	*1992/93p*
Contact with moving machinery	3	8	4	3	7	2	2
Struck by moving including flying/falling object	5	10	7	10	6	11	8
Struck by moving vehicle	3	10	14	8	22	11	4
Strike against something fixed or stationary	–	–	–	–	–	1	–
Injured while handling, lifting or carrying	–	–	1	1	–	1	–
Slip, trip or fall on same level	1	–	–	1	–	1	1
Fall from height	23	33	33	49	28	23	24
of which: Up to and including 2 m	1	2	2	8	3	2	1
Over 2 m	20	31	31	38	22	19	19
Height not stated	2	–	–	3	3	2	4
Trapped by something collapsing/overturning	4	12	7	20	5	4	9
Drowning or asphyxiation	4	1	4	3	2	2	3
Exposure to or contact with harmful substance	–	1	1	1	3	2	1
Exposure to fire	–	–	1	1	3	2	3
Exposure to an explosion	–	2	1	1	2	–	–
Contact with electricity or electrical discharge	7	5	5	5	4	9	4
Injured by an animal	1	2	2	1	2	2	1
Other kind of accident	1	–	–	–	3	–	–
Injuries not classified by kind	–	–	–	1	–	–	–
Total	52	84	80	105	87	71	60

1986/87	1987/88	1988/89	1989/90	1990/91	1991/92	1992/93p
39	50	76	69	65	72	70
103	119	187	203	200	166	163
27	55	66	57	46	54	51
12	19	21	21	25	19	16
26	37	36	52	47	35	40
65	73	121	146	178	118	142
322	393	505	605	626	522	482
101	130	156	194	167	173	162
207	235	310	367	388	285	255
14	28	39	44	71	64	65
28	37	37	49	50	25	39
–	5	4	3	1	2	2
14	12	18	14	24	19	18
3	11	12	16	4	10	6
1	8	7	2	–	4	11
30	20	32	33	30	29	16
6	11	14	8	8	4	14
14	17	16	25	21	22	20
–	–	–	7	1	–	–
690	867	1152	1310	1326	1101	1090

1986/87	1987/88	1988/89	1989/90	1990/91	1991/92	1992/93p
64	47	62	87	83	86	82
188	258	331	389	455	386	431
45	57	54	57	66	56	52
51	44	55	86	106	92	114
135	131	195	250	270	314	354
100	128	192	236	280	266	350
311	352	391	523	586	417	475
122	139	160	229	238	183	200
159	178	199	247	242	163	170
30	36	32	47	106	71	105
38	37	46	46	41	36	33
1	2	—	1	1	—	—
23	22	29	33	38	38	40
9	5	14	8	8	19	6
1	6	9	10	7	7	4
15	17	33	40	43	32	33
12	12	14	15	11	10	17
35	40	78	75	81	73	107
1	—	—	9	1	—	—
1029	1159	1503	1865	2077	1832	2098

p   provisional

67

Table 7   Injuries to employees by nature and severity of injury 1987/88 - 1992/93p
As reported to HSE's Field Operations Division Inspectorates (a) and local authorities

	Fatal					
	1987/88	*1988/89*	*1989/90*	*1990/91*	*1991/92*	*1992/93p*
Nature of injury						
Amputation	2	3	–	–	–	–
Loss of sight of eye	–	–	–	–	–	–
Fracture	74	47	56	46	31	23
Dislocation	–	–	–	–	–	–
Concussion and internal injuries	19	22	21	16	14	14
Lacerations and open wounds	6	10	3	3	2	3
Contusions	56	38	33	37	54	48
Burns	22	10	14	9	13	13
Poisonings and gassings	21	24	20	25	24	17
Sprains and strains	1	1	–	–	1	–
Superficial injuries	4	–	1	–	–	1
Natural causes	–	1	2	–	–	1
Other injuries caused by contact with electricity	15	12	19	19	8	17
Injuries of more than one type	30	64	54	37	41	32
Injuries not elsewhere classified	12	11	25	21	2	2
Injuries not known	47	67	89	85	65	56
Total	309	310	337	298	255	227

Non-fatal major							Over-3-day					
1987/88	*1988/89*	*1989/90*	*1990/91*	*1991/92*	*1992/93p*		*1987/88*	*1988/89*	*1989/90*	*1990/91*	*1991/92*	*1992/93p*
1840	1812	1725	1392	1120	1006		7	–	–	71	24	62
16	13	29	20	20	16		11	5	10	9	4	11
13 225	13 382	13 918	14 108	12 525	11 721		12 020	12 628	13 095	12 881	11 688	10 848
41	42	30	30	45	49		925	1051	1179	1116	1098	1068
141	142	175	147	138	130		1196	1210	1248	1127	1173	983
687	632	644	617	541	548		13 266	13 126	12 739	11 833	10 631	8896
371	373	413	371	331	378		25 726	27 229	29 365	28 813	26 692	23 678
911	814	868	859	843	711		4718	4890	5347	4959	4725	4103
215	189	286	224	186	249		412	424	504	573	533	478
186	169	111	153	158	125		54 571	55 942	59 600	59 599	58 862	53 967
357	288	259	263	232	233		17 679	17 807	18 184	17 215	16 683	15 466
7	3	4	5	4	5		16	8	8	15	7	10
92	69	71	80	64	84		191	176	231	219	200	232
242	257	255	261	230	196		1985	2129	2444	2440	3084	2972
64	77	75	68	80	70		857	878	1066	1139	1048	925
400	357	376	327	222	260		13 850	14 010	10 952	10 716	9009	8313
18 795	18 619	19 239	18 925	16 739	15 781		147 430	151 513	155 972	152 725	145 461	132 013

Notes
(a)   Data for the years prior to 1990/91 exclude reports made to HSE's Quarries Inspectorate.
p   provisional

Table 8 Injuries to the self-employed by nature and severity of injury 1987/88 - 1992/93p
As reported to HSE's Field Operations Division Inspectorates (a) and local authorities

			Fatal			
Nature of injury	1987/88	1988/89	1989/90	1990/91	1991/92	1992/93p
Amputation	3	1	–	–	–	–
Loss of sight of eye	–	–	–	–	–	–
Fracture	29	14	17	17	16	13
Dislocation	–	–	–	–	–	–
Concussion and internal injuries	4	3	9	2	5	4
Lacerations and open wounds	3	–	1	1	2	2
Contusions	7	8	10	15	9	12
Burns	3	2	2	5	4	4
Poisonings and gassings	2	8	3	8	8	3
Sprains and strains	–	–	–	–	–	–
Superficial injuries	–	–	–	–	–	–
Natural causes	–	–	1	2	2	–
Other injuries caused by contact with electricity	4	5	4	1	6	2
Injuries of more than one type	15	17	12	10	11	7
Injuries not elsewhere classified	2	2	7	3	–	–
Injuries not known	11	18	38	23	7	13
Total	83	78	104	87	70	60

		Non-fatal major						Over-3-day			
1987/88	*1988/89*	*1989/90*	*1990/91*	*1991/92*	*1992/93p*	*1987/88*	*1988/89*	*1989/90*	*1990/91*	*1991/92*	*1992/93p*
57	81	89	70	67	64	–	–	–	4	–	2
2	3	3	3	3	5	–	1	–	–	1	–
575	780	922	958	810	787	239	303	334	403	363	400
3	2	2	3	3	4	16	18	28	32	33	42
16	22	21	15	10	11	21	27	52	38	38	31
44	44	64	66	41	57	199	230	304	329	273	271
22	44	42	38	24	34	236	279	356	389	316	397
41	55	54	44	45	38	39	67	78	75	67	70
11	8	7	7	11	12	10	7	4	8	10	4
8	9	5	17	5	4	164	258	282	342	330	433
14	21	12	18	17	11	86	145	182	205	212	224
1	–	–	–	–	–	–	–	1	–	–	–
2	2	3	5	6	2	4	8	5	9	7	5
33	28	32	39	24	28	50	32	53	83	40	64
4	4	7	5	4	4	11	11	13	13	6	19
26	37	32	33	23	24	76	103	142	132	101	113
859	1140	1295	1322	1093	1085	1151	1489	1834	2062	1797	2075

Notes
(a)   Data for the years prior to 1990/91 exclude reports made to HSE's Quarries Inspectorate.
p   provisional

Table 9 Injuries to employees by site and severity of injury 1987/88-1992/93p
As reported to HSE's Field Operations Division Inspectorates (a) and local authorities

Site of injury	Fatal					
	1987/88	1988/89	1989/90	1990/91	1991/92	1992/93p
Eye	–	–	–	–	–	–
Ear	–	–	–	–	–	–
Other parts of face	–	–	1	–	–	–
Head (excluding face)	78	72	79	54	55	53
Several locations of head	5	9	9	8	7	3
Total: Head locations	83	81	89	62	62	56
Neck	6	8	5	6	4	5
Back	6	2	2	1	2	1
Trunk	28	28	33	25	23	27
Several locations of torso	3	4	2	6	3	4
Total: Torso locations	43	42	42	38	32	37
One or more finger/thumb(s)	1	–	1	–	1	–
Hand	1	–	–	–	–	–
Wrist	1	–	–	–	–	–
Rest of upper limb	1	–	1	1	2	–
Several locations of upper limb	–	–	–	–	–	1
Total: Upper limb locations	4		2	1	3	1
One or more toes	1	–	1	–	–	–
Foot	1	1	–	–	–	–
Ankle	2	2	3	–	1	–
Rest of lower limb	1	3	–	2	6	3
Several locations of lower limb	2	–	–	–	–	1
Total: Lower limb locations	7	6	4	2	7	4
Several locations	75	86	94	75	68	45
General locations	46	43	46	51	38	38
Unspecified locations	51	52	60	69	45	46
Total: All locations	309	310	337	298	255	227

Non-fatal major

1987/88	1988/89	1989/90	1990/91	1991/92	1992/93p
739	650	650	679	583	542
8	12	8	4	5	9
209	196	190	212	162	154
491	496	535	490	441	397
66	62	60	63	55	54
1513	1416	1443	1448	1246	1156
67	61	68	60	50	59
444	448	453	473	408	440
748	672	783	812	626	509
23	25	20	37	22	28
1282	1206	1324	1382	1106	1036
2219	2153	2089	1802	1492	1380
378	355	366	323	362	283
4054	4223	4360	4363	3959	3839
3109	3152	3254	3243	3070	2803
145	127	155	164	154	143
9905	10 010	10 224	9895	9037	8448
125	102	103	108	72	59
280	302	275	266	295	201
2281	2349	2424	2537	2303	2136
1969	1951	1985	1955	1647	1622
86	114	132	137	115	111
4741	4818	4919	5003	4382	4129
926	843	956	832	700	677
270	235	278	262	211	277
158	91	95	103	57	58
18 795	18 619	19 239	18 925	16 739	15 781

Over-3-day

1987/88	1988/89	1989/90	1990/91	1991/92	1992/93p
3687	3415	3686	3495	3376	2938
148	162	140	164	135	109
1475	1566	1694	1682	1532	1338
3621	3897	4069	3788	3734	3393
386	414	404	416	482	380
9317	9454	9993	9545	9259	8158
2019	2055	2147	2225	2089	1994
32 585	33 268	34 428	34 400	33 665	31 540
6879	6571	6949	6914	6341	5728
449	449	440	562	550	539
41 932	42 343	43 964	44 101	42 645	39 801
21 104	22 520	23 006	22 182	20 525	18 519
9666	10 197	10 500	10 394	9724	8575
4008	3953	4131	4058	3816	3399
11317	11 451	12 423	12 243	11 588	10 612
899	941	1053	1057	1081	951
46 994	49 062	51 113	49 934	46 734	42 056
3824	4016	4085	3787	3326	2734
9152	9438	10 024	9405	8633	7530
9197	9607	10 437	10 034	9823	8877
13 874	14 058	15 123	14 695	13 982	12 551
855	984	1054	1118	1100	1031
36 902	38 103	40 723	39 039	36 864	32 723
7844	8249	9030	8817	8745	8228
621	590	652	788	759	681
3820	3712	497	501	455	366
147 430	151 513	155 972	152 725	145 461	132 013

Notes
(a) Data for the years prior to 1990/91 exclude reports made to HSE's Quarries Inspectorate.
p provisional

Table 10   Injuries to the self-employed by site and severity of injury 1987/88-1992/93p
As reported to HSE's Field Operations Division Inspectorates (a) and local authorities
————————————————————— *Fatal* —————————

Site of injury	1987/88	1988/89	1989/90	1990/91	1991/92	1992/93
Eye	–	–	–	–	–	–
Ear	–	–	–	–	–	–
Other parts of face	–	–	–	–	1	–
Head (excluding face)	30	19	27	18	22	15
Several locations of head	1	1	2	1	–	2
Total: Head locations	31	20	29	19	23	17
Neck	4	1	1	2	3	2
Back	1	2	1	1	–	2
Trunk	9	9	10	4	4	8
Several locations of torso	1	1	–	1	–	–
Total: Torso locations	15	13	12	8	7	12
One or more finger/thumb(s)	–	–	–	–	1	–
Hand	–	–	–	–	–	–
Wrist	–	–	–	–	–	–
Rest of upper limb	1	1	–	–	–	–
Several locations of upper limb	–	–	–	–	–	–
Total: Upper limb locations	1	1			1	
One or more toes	–	–	–	–	–	–
Foot	–	–	–	–	–	–
Ankle	–	–	2	–	–	–
Rest of lower limb	2	1	2	1	3	1
Several locations of lower limb	2	–	–	–	–	–
Total: Lower limb locations	4	1	4	1	3	1
Several locations	15	23	22	24	16	11
General locations	10	14	9	12	17	8
Unspecified locations	7	6	28	23	3	11
Total: All locations	83	78	104	87	70	60

Non-fatal major

1987/88	1988/89	1989/90	1990/91	1991/92	1992/93p
21	27	29	46	27	33
2	1	–	2	–	2
13	15	14	13	9	21
51	76	87	57	46	49
2	3	3	3	4	3
89	**122**	**133**	**121**	**86**	**108**
8	7	6	4	2	3
39	38	47	56	36	38
48	72	73	68	63	55
3	3	3	5	2	1
98	**120**	**129**	**133**	**103**	**97**
71	84	99	86	70	77
8	22	21	26	17	17
87	128	171	182	136	152
118	174	183	203	183	182
9	8	18	10	10	11
293	**416**	**492**	**507**	**416**	**439**
7	6	9	7	9	7
18	29	25	24	25	15
83	125	159	147	150	144
122	167	180	205	158	145
11	10	13	15	12	15
241	**337**	**386**	**398**	**354**	**326**
123	133	140	147	114	96
8	9	6	8	16	16
7	3	9	8	4	3
859	**1140**	**1295**	**1322**	**1093**	**1085**

Over-3-day

1987/88	1988/89	1989/90	1990/91	1991/92	1992/93p
35	41	58	70	55	52
5	2	3	2	5	3
21	30	40	42	30	45
66	82	120	81	65	77
10	5	12	11	5	10
137	**160**	**233**	**206**	**160**	**187**
11	19	19	17	17	17
109	141	194	186	191	239
95	108	109	134	122	140
5	7	8	19	2	5
220	**275**	**330**	**356**	**332**	**401**
130	187	221	273	280	312
83	93	122	153	149	154
17	30	32	38	29	35
68	86	115	124	124	146
7	8	12	13	8	13
305	**404**	**502**	**601**	**590**	**660**
42	50	68	71	49	53
112	148	181	214	191	203
59	88	113	136	112	152
127	185	194	245	185	230
15	20	17	11	14	18
355	**491**	**573**	**677**	**551**	**656**
111	122	163	195	140	151
10	15	16	15	16	13
13	22	17	12	8	7
1151	**1489**	**1834**	**2062**	**1797**	**2075**

Notes
(a) Data for the years prior to 1990/91 exclude reports made to HSE's Quarries Inspectorate.
p   provisional

Table 11 Injuries to male employees by age of injured person and severity of injury 1986/87-1992/93p
As reported to HSE's Field Operations Division Inspectorates (a) and local authorities

	Fatal						
Age of injured person	1986/87	1987/88	1988/89	1989/90	1990/91	1991/92	1992/93p
Under 16	1	1	–	1	–	–	1
16-19	24	22	24	19	20	7	10
20-24	32	32	37	26	32	26	18
25-34	61	54	49	60	52	50	50
35-44	62	60	61	66	46	48	46
45-54	55	70	58	64	78	58	47
55-59	35	24	29	45	24	24	20
60-64	14	18	28	25	25	18	16
65+	1	3	4	10	5	4	5
Unknown	6	13	14	14	11	11	6
Total	291	297	304	330	293	246	219

Table 12 Injuries to female employees by age of injured person and severity of injury 1986/87-1992/93p
As reported to HSE's Field Operations Division Inspectorates (a) and local authorities

	Fatal						
Age of injured person	1986/87	1987/88	1988/89	1989/90	1990/91	1991/92	1992/93p
Under 16	–	–	–	–	–	–	–
16-19	–	–	1	–	1	–	1
20-24	2	2	–	–	–	1	–
25-34	–	–	1	1	–	1	2
35-44	–	1	1	2	2	1	1
45-54	1	–	1	4	–	3	1
55-59	–	–	–	–	1	2	1
60-64	3	–	1	–	–	–	1
65+	–	–	–	–	–	1	–
Unknown	–	–	–	–	1	–	1
Total	6	3	5	7	5	9	8

		Non-fatal major								Over-3-day				
1986/87	1987/88	1988/89	1989/90	1990/91	1991/92	1992/93p		1986/87	1987/88	1988/89	1989/90	1990/91	1991/92	1992/93p
33	14	18	19	13	11	6		28	23	33	24	29	11	19
1306	1381	1401	1324	1050	814	700		6525	6873	7078	7126	6311	5125	4096
1876	1864	1893	1880	1634	1474	1221		15 424	15 335	15 061	15 077	14 052	12 355	10 236
3045	3123	3143	3323	3279	2858	2717		30 056	30 283	31 297	32 152	31 945	29 935	27 006
2974	2841	2739	2715	2678	2510	2256		25 573	25 521	25 410	26 609	26 114	24 654	22 128
2594	2419	2421	2436	2442	2208	2225		20 336	19 812	20 087	21 205	20 510	19 665	18 606
1056	1087	959	1002	1046	886	787		8301	7855	7753	7878	7765	7154	6379
692	669	599	644	634	571	551		4904	4470	4696	4757	4542	4198	3594
69	58	61	70	87	61	64		117	104	114	188	178	190	171
1071	1171	1266	1402	1377	1148	1172		5889	6310	7218	7797	7808	7654	7325
14 716	14 627	14 500	14 815	14 240	12 541	11 699		117 153	116 586	118 747	122 813	119 254	110 941	99 560

Notes
(a) Data for the years prior to 1990/91 exclude reports made to HSE's Quarries Inspectorate.
p   provisional

		Non-fatal major								Over-3-day				
1986/87	1987/88	1988/89	1989/90	1990/91	1991/92	1992/93p		1986/87	1987/88	1988/89	1989/90	1990/91	1991/92	1992/93p
10	8	1	6	4	2	4		11	5	6	9	12	6	6
256	320	319	349	306	227	195		1780	1945	2079	2188	1942	1718	1320
343	403	352	379	366	384	311		3080	3462	3728	4060	3848	3763	3364
499	448	549	567	615	549	571		3923	4576	5297	5993	6422	6821	6379
711	656	625	711	744	641	681		5376	5868	6166	7182	7148	7433	7030
1045	1010	968	1032	1146	1006	973		6189	6306	6629	7352	7433	7877	7627
686	613	616	625	706	593	559		2537	2603	2534	2835	2803	2777	2588
207	208	236	257	274	282	277		560	613	663	793	847	892	922
74	63	43	46	64	56	64		42	44	62	60	80	92	70
380	377	379	449	459	456	447		1745	2059	2328	2667	2923	3128	3133
4211	4106	4088	4421	4684	4196	4082		25 243	27 481	29 492	33 139	33 458	34 507	32 439

Notes
(a) Data for the years prior to 1990/91 exclude reports made to HSE's Quarries Inspectorate.
p   provisional

Table 13 Injury rates for males (per 100 000 employees) by industrial sector 1988/89 -1992/93p
As reported to all enforcing authorities (a)

			Fatal		
Industrial sector	*1988/89*	*1989/90*	*1990/91*	*1991/92*	*1992/93p*
Agriculture	8.7	10.6	12.3	8.5	8.5
Energy	51.3	8.3	7.5	9.0	6.2
Manufacturing	2.6	3.0	2.5	2.2	1.9
Construction	11.3	10.8	10.6	10.0	8.7
Services	1.4	1.4	1.3	1.3	1.2
Total	4.3	3.0	2.7	2.6	2.1

Table 14 Injury rates for females (per 100 000 employees) by industrial sector 1988/89 -1992/93p
As reported to all enforcing authorities (a)

			Fatal		
Industrial sector	*1988/89*	*1989/90*	*1990/91*	*1991/92*	*1992/93p*
Agriculture	2.5	1.3	–	–	3.0
Energy	–	–	–	–	–
Manufacturing	0.1	0.1	0.1	–	0.2
Construction	–	–	0.7	–	–
Services	**	**	**	0.3	–
Total	**	0.1	**	0.2	0.1

Non-fatal major

1988/89	1989/90	1990/91	1991/92	1992/93p
176.7	175.3	190.4	168.4	188.4
310.8	301.0	279.8	265.4	236.0
177.6	176.4	164.9	156.6	150.3
321.7	340.9	321.1	301.6	279.6
68.7	69.7	70.0	70.2	65.3
132.4	133.5	126.4	120.2	110.6

Over-3-day

1988/89	1989/90	1990/91	1991/92	1992/93p
582.4	596.3	554.5	564.8	610.9
3400.7	3081.0	2764.9	2342.7	1983.3
1317.6	1404.0	1351.8	1366.9	1324.6
1842.3	1841.7	1847.3	1770.5	1590.8
723.5	733.0	725.1	698.2	643.3
1083.3	1099.4	1060.1	1018.5	936.1

Notes
(a) Excluding the Railway Inspectorate for which analysis by sex injured person is not readily available.
p   provisional

Non-fatal major

1988/89	1989/90	1990/91	1991/92	1992/93p
81.6	51.0	77.4	63.5	88.7
40.4	28.0	58.9	31.7	30.5
64.6	69.1	68.3	59.0	59.3
23.0	19.4	29.3	48.0	28.4
35.6	37.8	40.2	53.7	36.4
40.5	42.4	44.4	54.2	39.4

Over-3-day

1988/89	1989/90	1990/91	1991/92	1992/93p
252.2	335.9	263.6	291.0	371.4
338.0	305.0	295.7	232.9	198.2
568.1	640.0	607.2	625.3	581.0
88.7	102.7	142.9	181.2	118.6
242.4	262.9	272.7	288.1	279.1
293.1	317.2	318.5	330.4	314.3

Notes
**   Less than 0.05
(a) Excluding the Railway Inspectorate for which analysis by sex injured person is not readily available.
p   provisional

Table 15 Dangerous occurrences, 1986/87 - 1992/93p
As reported to all enforcement authorities

Reported to HSE Inspectorates	1986/87	1987/88	1988/89	1989/90	1990/91	1991/92	1992/93p
Part 1							
1 Failure, collapse or overturning of lifting machinery, excavator, pile driving frame or mobile powered access platform	886	831	888	911	782	709	729
2 Failure or collapse of passenger carrying amusement device or safety arrangement at a fair	16	16	23	15	13	13	21
3 Explosion, collapse or bursting of any closed vessel including boiler, above or below atmospheric pressure	247	209	178	165	170	149	158
4 Electrical fault causing fire or explosion and plant stoppage for over 24 hours	202	191	119	142	147	142	140
5 Explosion or fire due to ignition of process materials, waste or finished products and stoppage for over 24 hours	343	358	365	375	365	281	268
6 Uncontrolled release or escape of 1 tonne or more of highly flammable liquids or flammable gas	80	91	104	86	86	89	88
7 Collapse or part collapse of scaffold over 5 m high	76	97	104	115	79	77	74
8 Collapse or partial collapse of (a) any building or structure under construction involving over 5 tonnes of materials or (b) any floor or wall of a building used as a place of work	85	93	79	106	61	60	71
9 Uncontrolled or accidental release of potentially harmful substance or pathogen from certain equipment or sites	820	753	631	696	676	656	704
10 Unintentional ignition or explosion of explosives	76	82	137	137	184	151	93
11 Failure or collapse of a lifted freight container or part thereof	16	13	38	32	49	20	27

			1986/87	*1987/88*	*1988/89*	*1989/90*	*1990/91*	*1991/92*	*1992/93p*
12	Bursting, explosion or collapse of a pipeline or any part thereof or the ignition of anything in a pipeline (excluding water pipes)		114	96	74	93	75	75	68
13	Overturning or serious damage to the tank while conveying by road prescribed dangerous substances, or the uncontrolled release or fire involving the substance being conveyed		69	49	71	107	91	89	64
14	Uncontrolled release or escape of a dangerous substance, or a fire involving the dangerous substances, when being conveyed by road in a vehicle		32	21	35	44	42	42	38
15	Failure of breathing apparatus in service		31	33	36	54	69	59	68
16	Plant or equipment coming into contact unintentionally with overhead electric cables or causing an electrical discharge		252	235	250	220	189	216	239
17	Accidental collision between locomotive or train and other vehicle causing a reportable injury		23	17	15	21	45	21	22
Part 1	(Notifiable in relation to any place of work)	Total	3368	3185	3147	3319	3123	2849	2872
Part 2	(Notifiable in relation to mines)	Total	349	367	268	255	198	106	70
Part 3	(Notifiable in relation to quarries)	Total	27	30	25	25	18	9	17
Part 4	(Notifiable in relation to railways)	Total							
	Not elsewhere classified		149	233	290	341	321	379	324
		Total	3893	3815	3730	3940	3660	3343	3283
	Reported to local authorities		290	285	420	210	292	333	n/a
	Grand Total		4183	4100	4150	4150	3952	3676	n/a

Notes

(a) The table excludes occurrences in the oil and gas industry reported under offshore safety legislation.

(b) The table excludes occurrences notified to the Railway Inspectorate under the Railway (Notice of Accidents) Order. Full details of occurrences notified under this order can be found in the Department of Transport annual report on the safety record of the railways in Great Britain.

n/a not available
p   provisional

Table 16 Incidents relating to supply and use of flammable gas (a) 1986/87 - 1992/93p

	1986/87	*1987/88*	*1988/89*	*1989/90*	*1990/91*	*1991/92*	*1992/93p*
Number of incidents (b)							
Explosion/fire	60	71	45	68	43	50	31
Carbon monoxide poisoning	71	77	81	62	78	89	99
Total	131	148	126	130	122 (c)	140 (d)	130
Number of fatalities							
Explosion/fire	12	12	6	15	11	8	3
Carbon monoxide poisoning	35	48	41	34	30	33	39
Total	47	60	47	49	42 (c)	41	42
Number of non-fatalities							
Explosion/fire	58	72	42	67	48	63	33
Carbon monoxide poisoning	85	76	94	88	131	184	170
Total	143	148	136	155	179	249(d)	203

Notes
(a) Mainly piped gas but also includes bottled LPG.
(b) An incident can cause more than one fatality or injury.
(c) Includes one incident causing a fatality where the kind of incident is not known.
(d) Includes one incident causing two non-fatal injuries where kind of incident is not known.
p provisional

Table 17 Dangerous Gas Fitting Notifications: type of appliance 1986/87 - 1992/93p

	1986/87	*1987/88*	*1988/89*	*1989/90*	*1990/91*	*1991/92*	*1992/93p*
Boiler (including circulator)	187	169	521	729	771	613	428
Instantaneous water heater	50	27	67	94	90	45	49
Combined fire / boiler unit	45	48	138	205	189	148	87
Warm air unit	17	7	34	66	50	37	28
Gas fire (other than decorative / fuel effect)	305	190	296	295	279	272	210
Convector	24	6	13	17	19	11	19
Decorative gas log and other effect appliance	23	35	78	81	207	166	86
Cooking appliances	226	125	150	130	122	157	85
Other	62	36	41	54	55	48	32
Not known	68	42	42	36	24	27	32
Not applicable	424	356	449	327	301	240	163
Total	1431	1041	1829	2034	2107	1764	1219

p provisional

Table 18 Dangerous Gas Fitting Notifications: section of installation at fault 1986/87 - 1992/93p

	1986/87	1987/88	1988/89	1989/90	1990/91	1991/92	1992/93p
Service pipe	56	64	80	64	44	34	29
Gas meter	73	112	131	106	85	93	50
Installation pipe	537	324	412	353	381	305	194
Open flued appliance (including ventilation but excluding flue)	219	154	574	854	954	666	387
Room sealed appliance	61	35	116	155	142	129	109
Flueless appliance (including ventilation)	88	35	47	32	48	45	41
Flue (serving open-flued appliance)	241	187	309	338	346	340	289
Other	79	84	86	82	66	90	76
Not known	57	38	47	35	25	39	32
Not applicable	20	8	27	15	16	23	12
Total	1431	1041	1829	2034	2107	1764	1219

p provisional

Table 19 Dangerous Gas Fitting Notifications: reason for fault 1986/87 - 1992/93p

	1986/87	1987/88	1988/89	1989/90	1990/91	1991/92	1992/93p
Design	16	7	27	37	23	18	18
Construction	83	48	59	32	30	43	52
Manner of installation	589	491	1085	1358	1452	1126	757
Modification / alteration	249	237	343	341	292	298	156
Servicing / maintenance	53	55	73	46	76	86	71
Age / lack of servicing	96	10	18	12	23	17	19
Interference (outside agency)	47	36	34	39	26	31	28
Consumer misuse	21	19	11	11	14	10	9
Other	114	88	67	79	98	60	49
Not known	148	44	72	58	51	50	56
Not applicable	15	6	40	21	22	25	4
Total	1431	1041	1829	2034	2107	1764	1219

p provisional

Table 20 Dangerous Gas Fitting Notifications: type of hazard 1986/87 - 1992/93p

	1986/87	1987/88	1988/89	1989/90	1990/91	1991/92	1992/93p
Gas leak	752	405	508	410	446	425	284
Gas leak plus ignition (ie resultant fire / explosion)	45	50	31	28	38	33	24
Open flued or flueless appliances installed in a bathroom	51	45	102	143	181	190	114
Inadequate removal of products of combustion	287	214	419	408	463	427	330
Inadequate ventilation	29	31	317	517	458	278	176
Other	212	239	361	461	465	355	237
Not known	43	35	35	30	23	28	31
Not applicable	12	22	56	37	33	28	23
Total	1431	1041	1829	2034	2107	1764	1219

p provisional

Table 21 Enforcement notices issued by enforcement authorities, by type of notice 1981 - 1992/93p

Notices issued by type	HSE Inspectorates and HSC agencies (a)			
	Improvement	Deferred prohibition	Immediate prohibition	Total notices
1981	5921	212	1906	8039
1982	5620	198	1906	7724
1983	6070	213	2326	8609
1984	6038	214	2549	8801
1985	5585	250	2193	8028
1986/87	6577	196	2707	9480
1987/88	6631	234	4296	11 161
1988/89	6693	189	4664	11 546
1989/90	7610	200	4332	12 142
1990/91	8489	227	4022	12 738
1991/92	8395	222	3802	12 419
1992/93p	7434	198	4225	11 857

Local authorities				All enforcement authorities			
Improvement	*Deferred prohibition*	*Immediate prohibition*	*Total notices*	*Improvement*	*Deferred prohibition*	*Immediate prohibition*	*Total notices*
6394	196	873	7463	12 315	408	2779	15 502
7410	274	888	8572	13 030	472	2794	16 296
6195	197	1069	7461	12 265	410	3395	16 070
6200	185	790	7175	12 238	399	3339	15 976
5466	203	832	6501	11 051	453	3025	14 529
6740	300	1060	8100	13 317	496	3767	17 580
7560	290	1670	9520	14 191	524	5966	20 681
8290	230	1550	10 070	14 983	419	6214	21 616
8180	230	1810	10 220	15 790	430	6142	22 362
10 590	240	2200	13 030	19 079	467	6222	25 768
18 980	290	2410	21 680	27 375	512	6212	34 099
n/a	n/a	n/a	n/a	n/a	n/a	n/a	n/a

Notes
n/a   not available
(a)   Including action taken by enforcing authorities for the railways and offshore sectors prior to joining HSE.
p   provisional

Table 22   Enforcement notices issued by HSE's Field Operations Division Inspectorates (a) by industrial sector and type of notice 1986/87 - 1992/93p

Standard Industrial Classification(1980)		Agriculture forestry and fishing	Energy and water supply industries	Total manu-facturing industries	Construction	Service industries	Unclassified	All industries
TYPE OF NOTICE	Division	0	1	2-4	5	6-9		
Improvement	1986/87	3866	11	2065	102	448	76	6568
	1987/88	2992	10	2769	195	636	10	6612
	1988/89	2879	15	2882	151	655	2	6584
	1989/90	3161	13	3349	151	832	16	7522
	1990/91	3157	15	4157	298	830	5	8462
	1991/92	2824	18	4095	360	1027	16	8340
	1992/93p	2280	22	3701	227	1135	14	7379
Deferred prohibition	1986/87	106	–	51	14	19	5	195
	1987/88	101	–	48	25	36	1	211
	1988/89	47	–	73	13	17	–	150
	1989/90	45	1	101	8	22	2	179
	1990/91	76	1	104	11	33	1	226
	1991/92	95	1	74	13	37	2	222
	1992/93p	83	–	75	6	30	3	197
Immediate prohibition	1986/87	1125	9	462	925	144	34	2699
	1987/88	815	2	633	2657 (b)	161	9	4277
	1988/89	877	5	830	2585 (b)	204	6	4507
	1989/90	799	9	957	2143	238	10	4156
	1990/91	793	16	916	2027	206	7	3965
	1991/92	703	11	944	1795	294	21	3768
	1992/93p	715	21	949	2165	292	51	4193
Total notices	1986/87	5097	20	2578	1041	611	115	9462
	1987/88	3908	12	3450	2877 (b)	833	20	11 100
	1988/89	3803	20	3785	2749 (b)	876	8	11 241
	1989/90	4005	23	4407	2302	1092	28	11 857
	1990/91	4026	32	5177	2336	1069	13	12 653
	1991/92	3622	30	5113	2168	1358	39	12 330
	1992/93p	3078	43	4725	2398	1457	68	11 769

Notes
(a)   Data for the years prior to 1990/91 exclude notices issued by HSE's Quarries Inspectorate.
(b)   Reflects the major enforcement initiatives aimed at small construction sites during the period May 1987 to September 1988.
p   provisional

Table 23 Proceedings instituted by enforcement authorities, by result 1981 - 1992/93p

HSE Inspectorates and HSC agencies (a)	*Date of Hearing*											
	1981 (b)	*1982 (b)*	*1983*	*1984*	*1985*	*1986/87*	*1987/88*	*1988/89*	*1989/90*	*1990/91*	*1991/92*	*1992/93p*
Total informations laid	1892	2351	2238	2209	2321	2199	2337	2328	2653	2312	2424	2129
Informations where result recorded	1838	2261	2133	2130	2258	2120	2337	2328	2653	2312	2424	2129
Of which convictions	1654	2065	1941	1944	1915	1771	2053	2090	2289	1991	2126	1843
Average penalty per conviction (£)	189	233	252	313	436	410	792 (d)	541	783 (e)	903 (f)	1181 (g)	1384
Local authorities (c)												
Informations laid	516	468	511	585	451	613	725	731	713	645	783	n/a
Of which convictions	446	402	421	525	417	530	629	597	664	551	690	n/a

Notes

(a) Including action taken by enforcing authorities in the railway and offshore sectors prior to joining HSE.

(b) HSE's Factory, Agricultural, Mines and Quarries Inspectorates only.

(c) Penalty data not available.

(d) Includes fines totalling £750 000 imposed against BP. If these convictions are excluded the average fine for 1987/88 would be £427.

(e) Includes a fine of £100 000 imposed against Nobels Explosives. If this conviction is excluded the average fine for 1989/90 would be £739.

(f) Includes a fine of £100 000 imposed against Tate and Lyle (reduced from £250 000 on appeal). If this conviction is excluded the average fine for 1990/91 would be £853.

(g) Includes the fines of £100 000 imposed against both Shell UK Ltd and British Gas plc, and the fine of £250 000 against British Rail. The average fine without these convictions would be £970.

n/a not available

p   provisional

Table 24   Proceedings taken by HSE's Field Operations Division Inspectorates (a) by result and industrial sector 1986/87 - 1992/93p

Standard Industrial Classification(1980)		Agriculture forestry and fishing	Energy and water supply industries	Total manu-facturing industries	Construction	Service industries	Unclassified	All industries
	Division	0	1	2-4	5	6-9		
Informations laid	1986/87	423	20	820	624	193	88	2168
	1987/88	381	17	959	759	190	15	2321
	1988/89	302	9	1012	685	209	81	2298
	1989/90	367	9	1108	781	279	3	2547
	1990/91	334	11	876	746	308	3	2278
	1991/92	274	27	1056	746	289	15	2407
	1992/93p	287	22	842	695	243	7	2096
Convictions	1986/87	335	17	723	461	155	59	1750
	1987/88	310	14	893	654	153	15	2039
	1988/89	256	9	945	599	196	62	2067
	1989/90	327	9	998	658	247	3	2242
	1990/91	281	11	806	600	268	3	1969
	1991/92	254	22	958	604	257	14	2109
	1992/93p	238	18	772	571	206	7	1812
Average penalty per conviction (£)	1986/87	166	343	454	488	473	556	413
	1987/88	178	54 288 (b)	450	471	483	354	786 (c)
	1988/89	304	606	545	590	625	330	530
	1989/90	250	894	827	762	896	1333	732
	1990/91	297	1500	884 (d)	857	736	1217	776 (e)
	1991/92	327	14 289 (f)	855	1035	1359	425	1042 (g)
	1992/93p	359	8489	1383	1279	1523	397	1298

Notes
(a) Data for the years prior to 1990/91 exclude action taken by HSE's Quarries Inspectorate.
(b) Includes fines against BP totalling £750 000. The average fine without these convictions would be £836.
(c) Includes fines against BP totalling £750 000. The average fine without these convictions would be £420.
(d) Includes a fine of £100 000 against Tate and Lyle. The average fine without this conviction would be £761.
(e) Includes a fine of £100 000 against Tate and Lyle. The average fine without this conviction would be £726.
(f) Includes fines of £100 000 against both Shell UK Ltd and British Gas plc. The average fine without these convictions would be £5718.
(g) Includes fines of £100 000 against both Shell UK Ltd and British Gas plc. The average fine without these convictions would be £948.
p   provisional

Table 25 Prescribed industrial diseases other than those assessed by Special Medical Boards
(a): new cases of assessed disablement by disease 1986/87-1991/92(b)

Conditions due to physical agents (physical cause) Disease	Disease no	1986/87	1987/88	1988/89	1989/90	1990/91	1991/92p
Radiation effects	A1	–	2	–	–	8	3
Heat cataract	A2	2	2	3	7	10	3
Decompression sickness	A3	–	1	1	2	2	1
Cramp of hand or forearm	A4	13	11	14	18	46	52
Beat hand	A5	14	22	11	5	16	17
Beat knee	A6	37	138	97	74	151	269
Beat elbow	A7	6	11	4	16	20	31
Inflammation of tendons of the hand, forearm or associated tendon sheaths (Tenosynovitis)	A8	376	322	294	423	556	649
Miner's nystagmus	A9	–	1	–	–	–	1
Occupational deafness (d)	A10	1202	1261	1170	1128	1041	972
Vibration white finger (c)	A11	1366	1673	1056	2601	5401	2369

Conditions due to biological agents (caused by animal, plant or other living agent)

	Disease no	1986/87	1987/88	1988/89	1989/90	1990/91	1991/92p
Anthrax	B1	–	–	–	–	1	–
Infection by leptospira	B3	1	–	–	2	–	1
Tuberculosis	B5	13	3	5	–	3	3
Brucellosis	B7	2	–	1	2	1	1
Viral hepatitis	B8	5	3	1	1	2	4
Infection by streptococcus suis (c)	B9	3	–	–	–	1	–
Avian chlamydiosis (c)	B10a	n/a	n/a	–	–	1	–
Ovine chlamydiosis (c)	B10b	n/a	n/a	–	–	–	1
Q fever (c)	B11	n/a	n/a	–	–	1	–
Orf (c)	B12	n/a	n/a	n/a	n/a	n/a	2

Conditions due to chemical agents

	Disease no	1986/87	1987/88	1988/89	1989/90	1990/91	1991/92p
Poisoning by lead or compounds of lead	C1	3	1	–	–	2	2
Poisoning by manganese	C2	–	–	–	–	1	–
Poisoning by arsenic	C4	–	–	–	1	–	–
Poisoning by mercury or compound of mercury(e)	C5	3	–	–	–	–	–
Poisoning by carbon disulphide	C6	–	1	–	–	–	–
Poisoning by benzene or a homologue of benzene	C7	3	–	3	1	–	5
Poisoning by nitro-, amino-, or chloro-benzene or homologues	C8	–	–	13	3	–	–
Poisoning by dinitrophenol	C9	–	–	–	–	1	–
Poisoning by chlorinated napthalene	C13	–	–	–	1	–	–
Poisoning by acrylamide monomer (c)	C19	n/a	n/a	n/a	n/a	n/a	1

Conditions due to chemical agents (continued) Disease	Disease no	1986/87	1987/88	1988/89	1989/90	1990/91	1991/92p
Dystrophy of the cornea (including ulceration of the corneal surface) of the eye	C20	1	–	–	1	–	1
Localised new growth of skin	C21a	4	3	2	4	5	6
Squamous celled carcinoma of skin	C21b	4	3	2	5	–	2
Papilloma of the bladder	C23	21	21	7	8	16	21
Occupational vitiligo	C25	2	–	1	–	–	–
Liver/kidney damage due to carbon tetrachloride	C26	–	–	–	–	1	–
Peripheral neuropathy due to exposure to n-hexane or methyl n-butyl keytone (c)	C29	n/a	–	–	1	–	1

Miscellaneous conditions

	Disease no	1986/87	1987/88	1988/89	1989/90	1990/91	1991/92p
Inflammation/ulceration of mucous membrane of upper respiratory tract or mouth	D4	36	19	15	22	13	75
Dermatitis	D5	464	368	285	301	432	411
Adeno-carcinoma of nasal cavity/nasal carcinoma	D6	2	5	2	5	1	–
Total		3583	3871	2987	4632	7733	4904

Source: DSS

Notes

p   provisional.
(a) See Table 27.
(b) Years starting 1 October.
(c) The following diseases were prescribed after
     1 October 1983:

Disease no.	Date prescribed
A11	1 April 1985
B9	3 October 1983
C29	4 January 1988
B10a B10b B11	19 July 1989
B12 C19	26 September 1991

(d) Figures for occupational deafness are based on calendar years, that is Jan-Dec 1987 to Jan-Dec 1992
Figures have been revised for the years prior to 1990 to exclude unsuccessful appeals and references to Medical Appeal Tribunals which had been included in error in previously published statistics.
(e) The figure for 1989/90 has been revised from that recorded in error in last year's table.

n/a Not applicable

Table 26 Prescribed industrial diseases other than those assessed by Special Medical Boards
(a): new cases of assessed disablement by award status 1990/91 – 1991/92 (b)

Conditions due to physical agents (physical cause) Disease	Disease no	Claims assessed in 1990/91		Claims assessed in 1991/92p	
		1-13% (No benefit)	14%+ (Benefit paid)	1-13% (No benefit)	14% + (Benefit paid)
Radiation effects	A1	7	1	1	2
Heat cataract	A2	4	6	3	–
Decompression sickness	A3	–	2	1	–
Cramp of hand or forearm	A4	41	5	45	7
Beat hand	A5	16	–	16	1
Beat knee	A6	148	3	265	4
Beat elbow	A7	20	–	30	1
Inflammation of tendons of the hand, forearm or associated tendon sheaths (Tenosynovitis)	A8	492	64	544	105
Miner's nystagmus	A9	–	–	1	–
Occupational deafness (d)	A10	n/a	1041	n/a	972
Vibration White Finger (c)	A11	5370	31	2343	26
Conditions due to biological agents (caused by animal, plant or other living agent)					
Anthrax	B1	1	–	–	–
Infection by leptospira	B3	–	–	–	1
Tuberculosis	B5	2	1	2	1
Brucellosis	B7	1	–	–	1
Viral hepatitis	B8	–	2	3	1
Infection by streptococcus suis (c)	B9	–	1	–	–
Avian chlamydiosis (c)	B10a	–	1	–	–
Ovine chlamydiosis (c)	B10b	–	–	–	1
Q fever (c)	B11	–	1	–	–
Orf (c)	B12	n/a	n/a	2	–
Conditions due to chemical agents					
Poisoning by lead or compounds of lead	C1	2	–	2	–
Poisoning by manganese	C2	–	1	–	–
Poisoning by arsenic	C4	–	–	–	–
Poisoning by mercury or compound of mercury	C5	–	–	–	–
Poisoning by carbon disulphide	C6	–	–	–	–
Poisoning by benzene or a homologue of benzene	C7	–	–	3	2
Poisoning by nitro-, amino-, or chloro-benzene or homologues	C8	–	–	–	–
Poisoning by dinitrophenol	C9	1	–	–	–
Poisoning by chlorinated napthalene	C13	–	–	–	–
Poisoning by acrylamide monomer (c)	C19	n/a	n/a	1	–

Conditions due to chemical agents (continued) Disease	Disease no	Claims assessed in 1990/91		Claims assessed in 1991/92p	
		1-13% (No benefit)	14%+ (Benefit paid)	1-13% (No benefit)	14%+ (Benefit paid)
Dystrophy of the cornea (including ulceration of the corneal surface) of the eye	C20	–	–	1	–
Localised new growth of skin	C21a	5	–	5	1
Squamous celled carcinoma of skin	C21b	–	–	1	1
Papilloma of the bladder	C23	3	13	9	12
Occupational vitiligo	C25	–	–	–	–
Liver/kidney damage from carbon tetrachloride	C26	–	1	–	–
Peripheral neuropathy due to exposure to n-hexane or methyl n-butyl keytone (c)	C29	–	–	–	1
Miscellaneous conditions					
Inflammation/ulceration of mucous membrane of upper respiratory tract or mouth	D4	13	–	74	1
Dermatitis	D5	407	25	379	32
Adeno-carcinoma of nasal cavity/nasal carcinoma	D6	1	–	–	–
Total		6534	1199	3731	1173

Note
See footnotes to Table 25.

Source: DSS

Table 27   Prescribed industrial diseases assessed by Special Medical Boards: new cases of assessed disablement by disease 1983-92

Disease	Disease no	1983	1984	1985	1986	1987	1988	1989	1990	1991	1992
Farmer's Lung	B6	8	4	6	11	8	15	13	7	5	5
Poisoning by nitrous fumes	C15	1	–	–	–	3	–	–	–	–	1
Beryllium poisoning	C17	1	–	–	2	4	3	–	2	1	–
Cadmium poisoning	C18	4	1	2	3	3	2	–	2	5	4
Primary carcinoma of bronchus or lung in nickel workers	C22b	1	5	2	3	–	–	–	1	2	1
Pneumoconiosis (a)	D1	670	577	702	747	652	562	661	709	751	765
Byssinosis (a)	D2	72	56	37	26	23	13	15	18	7	4
Diffuse mesothelioma	D3	148	201	245	305	399	479	441	462	519	551
Occupational asthma (b,c)	D7	183	137	166	166	220	222	220	216	293	553
Lung cancer in asbestos workers (c)	D8	n/a	n/a	8	34	55	59	54	58	55	54
Bilateral pleural thickening (c)	D9	n/a	n/a	61	111	115	114	125	146	149	160
Lung cancer (c)	D10	n/a	n/a	n/a	n/a	–	–	4	5	4	5
Total		1088	981	1229	1408	1482	1469	1533	1626	1791	2103

Source: DSS

Notes
(a) See also Tables 28 and 29.
(b) See also Table 30.
(c) The following diseases were prescribed after 1 January 1982.

Disease No.	Date Prescribed
D7	29 March 1982
D8	1 April 1985
D9	1 April 1985
D10	1 April 1987

n/a Not applicable.

Table 28   Pneumoconiosis and Byssinosis : new cases diagnosed by Special Medical Boards (Respiratory Diseases) (a) by industry to which the disease was attributed (b) 1983-92

Industrial Injuries Scheme Cases	1983	1984	1985	1986	1987	1988	1989	1990	1991	1992
Pneumoconiosis										
Coal mining	402	330	364	357	325	299	339	344	379	383
Other mining and quarrying:										
Slate	12	8	7	11	6	3	8	5	3	2
Other-except refractories	5	7	1	12	12	9	3	9	2	2
Asbestos (c)	199	186	273	312	247	202	268	306	330	354
Foundry workers:										
Iron foundry workers	10	13	17	17	13	12	10	9	11	5
Steel foundry workers	7	–	1	1	5	6	6	4	1	2
Non-ferrous foundry workers	–	1	–	1	1	2	–	3	–	–
Steel dressers	5	3	6	2	2	3	2	–	2	2
Pottery manufacture	14	9	14	10	18	11	9	6	8	4
Refractories (d)	5	5	3	6	3	6	4	7	–	2
Other attributable industries	11	15	16	18	20	9	12	16	15	9
Total	670	577	702	747	652	562	661	709	751	765
Byssinosis										
Cotton	67	53	36	25	23	13	15	n/a	n/a	n/a
Flax	5	3	1	1	–	–	–	n/a	n/a	n/a
Total	72	56	37	26	23	13	15	18	7	4
Cases diagnosed by Medical Appeal Tribunals										
Pneumoconiosis (excluding asbestosis)	25	30	21	28	36	32	26	n/a	n/a	n/a
Asbestosis	13	14	28	17	35	23	12	n/a	n/a	n/a
Byssinosis	2	7	–	1	2	2	–	n/a	n/a	n/a
Total	40	51	49	46	73	57	38	n/a	n/a	n/a
PBMDB scheme cases (e)										
Pneumoconiosis and byssinosis	44	30	18	17	28	20	18	14	26	17
Overall total: Pneumoconiosis and Byssinosis	826	714	806	836	776	652	732	741	784	786

Source: DSS

Notes
(a)   Formerly known as Pneumoconiosis Medical Panels.
(b)   The industry to which the disease is attributable is in some cases defined occupationally.
(c)   Cases where mesothelioma was also diagnosed are excluded, and shown in Table 27.
(d)   Including the mining, quarrying and processing of refractory material.
(e)   The figures of Pneumoconiosis, Byssinosis and Miscellaneous Diseases Benefits scheme cases refer to years ending September 30.
n/a   no longer available.

Table 29 Pneumoconiosis: new industrial injuries scheme cases diagnosed by Special Medical Boards (Respiratory Diseases) (a) in coal mining, asbestos and other industries, by age and percentage disablement (b) 1989 - 1992

Age	Coal mining					Asbestos workers (c)				
	Percentage disablement assessed					Percentage disablement assessed				
	10 or less	20 30 40	50 60 70	80 90 100	Total	10 or less	20 30 40	50 60 70	80 90 100	Total
1989										
Under 45	3	0	0	0	3	1	3	0	0	4
45-64	51	15	0	3	69	24	100	9	8	141
65+	94	150	19	4	267	24	73	14	12	123
Total	148	165	19	7	339	49	176	23	20	268
1990										
Under 45	1	0	0	0	1	1	0	0	1	2
45-64	40	22	3	1	66	29	98	7	12	146
65+	117	135	21	4	277	29	104	14	11	158
Total	158	157	24	5	344	59	202	21	24	306
1991										
Under 45	1	0	0	0	1	1	0	1	1	3
45-64	41	22	1	0	64	35	97	4	8	144
65+	120	165	22	7	314	33	122	10	18	183
Total	162	187	23	7	379	69	219	15	27	330
1992										
Under 45	1	0	0	0	1	2	3	0	0	5
45-64	53	22	2	0	77	40	106	2	11	159
65+	114	160	26	5	305	42	109	13	26	190
Total	168	182	28	5	383	84	218	15	37	354

Other

Percentage disablement assessed

10 or less	20 30 40	50 60 70	80 90 100	Total
1	0	0	0	1
10	11	0	1	22
10	14	4	3	31
21	25	4	4	54

10 or less	20 30 40	50 60 70	80 90 100	Total
3	1	0	0	4
8	7	1	0	16
14	21	3	1	39
25	29	4	1	59

10 or less	20 30 40	50 60 70	80 90 100	Total
0	1	1	0	2
8	7	0	1	16
8	14	2	0	24
16	22	3	1	42

10 or less	20 30 40	50 60 70	80 90 100	Total
0	0	0	0	0
5	2	0	0	7
7	12	1	1	21
12	14	1	1	28

Total

Percentage disablement assessed

10 or less	20 30 40	50 60 70	80 90 100	Total
5	3	0	0	8
85	126	9	12	232
128	237	37	19	421
218	366	46	31	661

10 or less	20 30 40	50 60 70	80 90 100	Total
5	1	0	1	7
77	127	11	13	228
160	260	38	16	474
242	388	49	30	709

10 or less	20 30 40	50 60 70	80 90 100	Total
2	1	2	1	6
84	126	5	9	224
161	301	34	25	521
247	428	41	35	751

10 or less	20 30 40	50 60 70	80 90 100	Total
3	3	0	0	6
98	130	4	11	243
163	281	40	32	516
264	414	44	43	765

Source: DSS

Notes
(a) See footnote to Table 28.
(b) Under a special provision a person found to be suffering from pneumoconiosis qualifies for a pension at the 10% rate even if he or she has no discernible respiratory disablement arising from the disease.
(c) Cases where mesothelioma was also diagnosed are excluded, and shown in Table 27.

Table 30 Occupational asthma: new cases of assessed disablement, by causative agent and percentage disability 1983-1992

	Agent		1983	1984	1985	1986	1987	1988	1989	1990	1991	1992
(a)	Isocyanates	1	74	51	46	48	60	64	72	73	95	121
	Platinum salts	2	9	4	9	12	9	12	6	5	3	3
	Hardening agents	3	12	14	19	28	18	31	24	22	34	64
	Soldering flux	4	24	27	25	20	21	24	30	23	35	37
	Proteolytic enzymes	5	3	1	6	0	6	2	3	3	3	1
	Animals/insects	6	7	8	7	12	7	9	9	7	10	10
	Flour/grain	7	54	32	54	46	50	40	43	55	64	60
	Total 1-7		183	137	166	166	171	182	187	188	244	296
(b)	Antibiotics	8					30	6	4	2	5	8
	Wood dusts	10					15	28	25	23	40	52
	Ispaghula	11					0	0	1	0	0	0
	Castor bean dust	12					0	0	0	0	1	0
	Ipecacuanha	13					0	1	0	0	0	0
	Azodicarbonamide	14					4	5	3	3	3	12
	Total 8-14						49	40	33	28	49	72
(c)	Animals/insects (larval forms)	15										2
	Glutaraldehyde	16										13
	Persulphate salts and henna	17										6
	Crustaceans	18										7
	Reactive dyes	19										5
	Soya bean dust	20										2
	Tea dust	21										5
	Fumes from stainless steel welding	23										16
	Open category	24										129
	Total 15-24											185
	Total agents 1-24		183	137	166	166	220	222	220	216	293	553

	Claims assessed in 1983-86			Claims assessed in 1987-92		
	13% or less	14-49%	50%+	13% or less	14-49%	50%+
Isocyanates	165	51	3	134	340	11
Platinum salts	31	3	0	17	21	0
Hardening agents	45	25	3	47	139	7
Soldering flux	61	31	4	21	139	10
Proteolytic enzymes	4	6	0	3	13	2
Animals/insects	26	7	1	14	37	1
Flour/grain	120	61	5	75	221	16
Total 1-7	452	184	16	311	910	47
Antibiotics				18	36	1
Wood dusts				41	132	10
Ispaghula				0	1	0
Castor bean dust				0	1	0
Ipecacuanha				0	1	0
Azodicarbonamide				10	19	1
Total 8-14				69	190	12
Total agents 1-14	452	184	16	380	1100	59

	Claims assessed in 1992		
	13% or less	14-49%	50%+
Animals/insects (larval forms)	1	1	0
Glutaraldehyde	5	8	0
Persulphate salts and henna	1	5	0
Crustaceans	4	3	0
Reactive dyes	2	3	0
Soya bean dust	0	2	0
Tea dust	0	5	0
Fumes from stainless steel welding	2	13	1
Open category	40	81	8
Total agents 15-24	55	121	9

Notes

There have been no awards for the following agents:
(9)Cimetidine (prescribed 1 September 1988 (22) Green coffee bean dust (prescribed 26 September 1991).
From 1 October 1986 cases with 13% or less disability do not qualify for benefit.
(a)   Agents prescribed from the start of the prescription.
(b)   Agents added to prescribed list with effect from 1 September 1986.
(c)   Agents added to prescribed list with effect from 26 September 1991.

Table 31   Cases of occupational disease reported under RIDDOR 1986/87 - 1992/93 (a)

Disease		1986/87	1987/88	1988/89	1989/90	1990/91	1991/92	1992/93 p	Corresponding DSS PD Number
Poisoning by									
Acrylamide	1a	–	–	–	–	–	–	–	C19
Arsenic	1b	–	1	2	–	–	–	–	C4
Benzene	1c	–	1	–	1	1	1	1	C7
Beryllium	1d	–	–	–	3	–	–	–	C17
Cadmium	1e	1	1	2	1	3	1	–	C18
Carbon disulphide	1f	–	–	–	–	–	–	–	C6
Diethylene dioxide	1g	–	–	–	–	–	–	–	C11
Ethylene oxide	1h	–	–	–	–	–	–	–	
Lead	1i	3	5	6	4	1	4	–	C1
Manganese	1j	–	–	–	–	–	1	–	C2
Mercury	1k	2	1	–	–	–	–	1	C5
Methyl bromide	1l	–	2	–	1	1	–	–	C12
Nitrochlorobenzene	1m	3	–	2	1	2	1	1	C8
Oxides of nitrogen	1n	–	1	–	1	–	–	1	C15
Phosphorous	1o	4	2	3	2	1	1	1	C3
Chrome ulcer	2	11	19	14	6	13	11	2	*
Folliculitis	3	5	1	1	–	1	1	–	*
Acne	4	–	1	–	1	–	–	–	*
Skin cancer	5	3	–	1	4	4	2	–	C21
Radiation skin injury	6	–	6	2	1	4	1	7	part A1
Occupational asthma	7	70	45	61	57	69	69	63	D7
Extrinsic alveolitis	8	4	13	7	5	7	2	6	B6
Pneumoconiosis	9	13	5	4	6	4	3	3	part D1
Byssinosis	10	–	–	1	2	–	3	–	D2
Mesothelioma	11	7	13	9	4	13	9	7	D3
Lung cancer (asbestos)	12	1	1	–	–	–	–	–	D8
Asbestosis	13	11	14	–	10	4	5	7	part D1
Lung cancer (nickel)	14	–	–	–	–	–	–	–	C22b
Leptospirosis	15	5	12	7	9	2	14	10	B3
Hepatitis	16	28	25	23	20	24	47	15	B8
Tuberculosis	17	14	11	7	7	9	8	12	B5
Pathogenic infection	18	20	6	16	15	20	28	17	–
Anthrax	19	–	–	–	–	–	1	–	B1
Bone cancer	20	–	–	–	–	–	–	–	part A1
Blood dyscrasia	21	1	–	–	–	–	3	2	
Cataract	22	3	7	–	–	2	–	–	A2

Disease		1986/87	1987/88	1988/89	1989/90	1990/91	1991/92	1992/93 p	Corresponding DSS PD Number
Decompression sickness	23	–	25	71	34	2	42	17	A3
Barotrauma	24	–	–	1	–	–	–	1	–
Nasal/sinus cancer	25	–	1	–	2	2	–	2	C22a\D6
Angiosarcoma	26	–	–	–	–	–	–	2	C24a
Urinary tract cancer	27	–	6	1	4	–	3	–	C23
Vibration White Finger	28	70	111	68	120	120	131	97	A11
Total		279	336	309	321	309	392	275	

Notes
p   provisional
(a)   Years starting April.
*   These three RIDDOR categories form part of DSS PD D5 (dermatitis), not separately
       identifiable in DSS figures. Dermatitis in general is not reportable under RIDDOR.

The data in this table record the extent of the employer reporting of diseases scheduled under RIDDOR, not the incidence of the diseases themselves. Comparison with other information sources - themselves incomplete - show that the number of cases reported under RIDDOR clearly understates the real incidence of work-related disease.

Table 32   Death certificates mentioning specified asbestos-related disease 1968-1991

							Year of death			
	Disease	1968	1969	1970	1971	1972	1973	1974	1975	1976	1977
	Asbestosis										
A	Together with lung cancer	25	24	26	32	44	43	33	49	53	59
B	Together with mesothelioma	32	27	40	29	40	30	65	50	74	53
C	Alone or together with other diseases	23	27	21	33	24	34	41	48	63	73
	Total A + C	48	51	47	65	68	77	74	97	116	132
	Total asbestosis deaths (A+B+C)	80	78	87	94	108	107	139	147	190	185
	Mesothelioma										
	Of pleura	98	105	115	104	125	138	146	169	198	212
	Of peritoneum	14	15	11	12	19	25	20	19	31	22
	Of pleura and peritoneum	3	3	2	4	0	3	3	5	4	6
	Site not specified	38	36	64	58	67	57	76	78	82	96
D	**Total mesothelioma deaths (includes B above)**	153	159	192	178	211	223	245	271	315	336
	Males	115	123	143	139	168	181	187	219	258	276
	Females	38	36	49	39	43	42	58	52	57	60
	Total number of deaths (A+C+D)	201	210	239	243	279	300	319	368	431	468

1978	1979	1980	1981	1982	1983	1984	1985	1986	1987	1988	1989	1990	1991p
60	46	56	77	75	60	60	66	84	59	78	75	76	57
85	76	69	65	79	89	86	87	65	109	89	97	120	86
49	56	46	60	53	61	69	74	82	85	74	82	88	106
109	102	102	137	128	121	129	140	166	144	152	157	164	163
194	178	171	202	207	210	215	227	231	253	241	254	284	249
235	263	259	308	325	412	476	411	378	471	453	481	500	701
31	34	38	24	28	33	43	32	40	39	48	44	53	50
13	6	7	5	16	9	10	13	12	14	17	12	9	18
111	131	155	135	135	124	97	159	272	284	344	362	319	248
390	434	459	472	504	578	626	615	702	808	862	899	881	1017
327	341	356	398	413	483	540	531	601	702	751	767	764	867
63	93	103	74	91	95	86	84	101	106	111	132	117	150
499	536	561	609	632	699	755	755	868	952	1014	1056	1045	1180

p provisional

Table 33   Death certificates mentioning mesothelioma by age and sex 1968 - 1991

Age group	1968-70	1971-73	1974-76	1977-79	1980-82	1983-85	1986-88	1989-91p
Males								
0-44	25	27	30	45	57	50	67	65
45-54	61	90	132	159	156	199	260	287
55-64	165	166	226	279	383	524	623	695
65-74	94	153	213	320	390	482	699	850
75+	36	52	63	141	181	299	405	501
Total	381	488	664	944	1167	1554	2054	2398
Females								
0-44	15	6	12	13	19	15	16	13
45-54	22	20	22	15	29	17	22	46
55-64	34	40	49	71	82	66	82	77
65-74	38	39	64	73	94	107	121	161
75+	14	19	20	44	44	60	77	102
Total	123	124	167	216	268	265	318	399
Total	504	612	831	1160	1435	1819	2372	2797

p provisional

Table 34   Mesothelioma crude death rates (per million) by region 1983-1991

Region	Males 1983-85	Males 1986-88	Males 1989-91	Females 1983-85	Females 1986-88	Females 1989-91
North	43.59	53.62	51.13	5.88	8.03	6.13
Yorkshire and Humberside	16.17	20.35	26.64	3.18	4.11	5.66
North West	19.99	23.07	27.40	3.78	4.50	5.09
West Midlands	7.70	9.10	12.66	1.78	2.15	2.26
East Midlands	15.73	18.19	23.08	3.38	3.16	3.60
South West	22.90	30.08	35.73	1.88	2.53	4.83
East Anglia	12.57	20.28	25.96	3.37	2.60	5.71
South East (excluding Greater London)	24.71	32.40	33.45	3.33	3.71	4.04
Greater London	16.35	22.94	27.99	4.29	4.49	6.29
Wales	9.55	14.76	18.12	1.15	1.60	2.25
Scotland	19.87	31.05	38.70	1.88	3.54	5.19
Great Britain	**19.38**	**25.40**	**29.35**	**3.13**	**3.73**	**4.64**

Table 35 Deaths due to occupationally-related lung disease, other than asbestos (a) 1981-1991

	1981	*1982*	*1983*	*1984*	*1985*	*1986*	*1987*	*1988*	*1989*	*1990*	*1991*
Pneumoconiosis (other than asbestos)	341	314	317	314	324	337	279	281	317	328	287
Byssinosis	26	22	33	24	25	29	25	22	25	19	16
Farmer's Lung and other occupational allergic alveolitis	13	15	15	10	7	15	16	9	8	6	8
Total	380	351	365	348	356	381	320	312	350	353	311

Source: OPCS

Note
(a) The data in this table is derived from death certificates. The figure is the number of deaths coded to the disease as underlying cause.

Table 36 Lead workers under medical surveillance 1986 to 1991/92

Maximum measured blood-lead µg/100ml	1986 Males	1986 Females	1987/88 Males	1987/88 Females	1988/89 Males	1988/89 Females
<40	15 912	1375	15 310	1300	16 820	1240
40<60	5206	138	4819	97	4751	66
60<70	1190	15	1241	21	1038	6
70<80	477	11	523	4	441	1
80 and over	217	4	239	1	196	0
Total under surveillance	23 002	1543	22 132	1423	23 246	1313
of which 70 and over	694	15	762	5	637	1
Individuals suspended	351	57	388	33	340	12

Table 37 Lead workers under medical surveillance, by sex, blood-lead level and industry sector 1991/92

	Males — Percentage in blood-lead category (µg/100ml)					Females — Number in category		
	<40	40-59	60-69	70+	Total under surveillance	<40	40+	Total under surveillance
Smelting, refining, alloying, casting	61.0	32.5	5.5	0.9	7759	115	1	116
Lead battery industry	56.9	33.9	6.6	2.5	4297	88	28	116
Badge and jewellery enamelling and other vitreous enamelling	100.0	0.0	0.0	0.0	58	27	0	27
Glass making	66.6	28.7	4.4	0.3	1059	168	5	173
Manufacture of pigments and colours	90.7	8.1	1.0	0.2	517	89	2	91
Potteries, glazes and transfers	87.8	11.0	1.2	0.0	425	166	4	170
Manufacture of inorganic and organic lead compounds	97.9	1.9	0.0	0.1	2288	6	0	6
Shipbuilding, repairing and breaking	91.8	6.8	1.0	0.3	293	1	0	1
Demolition industry	72.1	17.9	4.7	5.3	513	0	0	0
Painting buildings and vehicles	94.3	5.0	0.5	0.1	799	0	0	0
Work with metallic lead and lead containing alloys	78.2	18.5	2.5	0.8	2063	94	11	105
Other processes	90.8	7.3	1.0	0.8	3730	158	1	159
Scrap industry	57.6	25.4	9.0	7.9	177	0	0	0
All sectors	73.1	22.0	3.8	1.2	23978	912	52	964

1989/90		1990/91		1991/92	
Males	*Females*	*Males*	*Females*	*Males*	*Females*
16 195	1216	18 447	1175	17 531	912
4713	82	5413	68	5266	45
947	6	1132	7	905	1
366	0	274	1	192	0
168	0	178	1	84	6
22 389	1304	25 444	1252	23 978	964
534	0	452	2	276	6
286	21	260	26	153	13

ANNEX IV:
REFERENCES

1 *Health and Safety Statistics 1988-89*, Employment Gazette Occasional Supplement No 1, Employment Gazette Vol 98 No 11, November 1990.

2 *Health and Safety Statistics 1989-90*, Employment Gazette Occasional Supplement No 2, Employment Gazette Vol 99 No 9, September 1991.

3 *Health and Safety Statistics 1990-91*, Employment Gazette Occasional Supplement No 3, Employment Gazette Vol 100 No 9, September 1992.

4 Stevens, G *Workplace injury: a view from HSE's trailer to the 1990 Labour Force Survey* Employment Gazette Vol 100 No 12, December 1992.

5 HSE Research Paper 33 *Self-reported work-related illness* 1993 HSE Books ISBN 0 7176 0607 4

6 de Vos Irvine H et al Asbestos and lung cancer in Glasgow and the west of Scotland 1993 *BMJ* **306**: 1503-6

7 R Doll and R Peto *The Causes of Cancer: quantitative estimate of avoidable risks of cancer in the United States today* 1981 OUP ISBN 0 19 261359 6

8 Meredith S K, Taylor V M, McDonald J C Occupational respiratory disease in the United Kingdom 1989: a report to the British Thoracic Society and the Society of Occupational Medicine by the SWORD project group 1991 *British Journal of Industrial Medicine* **48**: 292-298

9 Meredith S K, Reported incidence of occupational asthma in the UK 1989-90 *Journal of Epidemology and Community Health* 1993 (in press)

10 Raw G J *Sick building syndrome: a review of the evidence on causes and solutions* HSE Contract Research Report 42/1992 HSE Books ISBN 0 11 886364 9

11 General Register Office *Morbidity Statistics from General Practice: Studies on medical and population subjects No 14* 1955-56 (out of print)

12 Royal College of General Practitioners *Morbidity Statistics from General Practice 1970-71 socio-economic analyses* 1982 HMSO ISBN 0 11 690910 2 (out of print)

13 Office of Population Censuses and Surveys, Department of Health and Social Security *Morbidity Statistics from General Practice* 1981-82: *third national study: microfiche* 1986 HMSO ISBN 0 11 690756 8 (out of print)

14 Kyriakides K *Survey of exposure to hand-arm vibration in Great Britain* HSE Research Paper 26 1988 HSE Books ISBN 0 11 885932 3

15 Bednall A W S*urvey of exposure to hand-arm vibration in Great Britain: mines and quarries* HSE Research Paper 29 1991 HSE Books ISBN 0 11 885900 5

16 Benn T Estimation of the prevalence of hand-arm vibration syndrome in Great Britain *Proceedings of the Institute of Acoustics* 1993 **15**: 463-470 (in press)

Printed in the UK for the Health and Safety Executive   11/93 C50